CELTIC
HYMN BOOK

FULL MUSIC

SELECTED BY RAY SIMPSON
MUSIC EDITOR KEITH DUKE

kevin
mayhew

Acknowledgements

The publishers wish to express their gratitude to the copyright holders who have granted permission to include their material in this book.

Every effort has been made to trace the copyright holders of all the songs in this collection and we hope that no copyright has been infringed. Apology is made and pardon sought if the contrary be the case, and a correction will be made in any reprint of this book.

First published in Great Britain in 2005 by
KEVIN MAYHEW LIMITED
Buxhall, Stowmarket, Suffolk IP14 3BW
Website: kevinmayhewltd.com
email: sales@kevinmayhewltd.com

Compilation © Kevin Mayhew Ltd 2005

The following editions are available: *0 1 2 3 4 5 6 7 8 9*

Full Music	Catalogue No: 1413262	ISBN: 1 84417 398 4	ISMN: M 57024 439 3
Melody	Catalogue No: 1413263	ISBN: 1 84417 443 3	ISMN: M 57024 479 9

Printed and bound in Great Britain

Introduction

The one who sings prays twice
A Jewish proverb

Celtic songs and poems are for every area of life. The hymn books of the last two centuries, in contrast, have been restricted to a 'church' box. This collection tries to break out of that box and provide hymns, songs and chants for all types of people and all sorts of occasions.

Celtic spirituality today weaves together God-given strands of Christianity which became separated in the second millennium, and which produced separate hymn books. This hymn book does some weaving.

Celtic hymnody has roots. The current world-wide resurgence of ethnic music and primal sounds seems to leave much church music high and dry. The Celtic tradition, with its roots in biblical and ancient worship, connects with this resurgence.

What are Celtic hymns?

The current rise of 'Celtic' worship songs is rightly not restricted to the so-called 'six Celtic nations' of Brittany, Cornwall, Ireland, Isle of Man, Wales and Scotland, although these figure predominantly. For one thing, the Celts originated in Asia and spread throughout Europe's heartlands; for another, Celtic Missions such as that of Aidan to English-speaking people introduced a distinctive spirituality to races that were not Celtic. Features which are distinctive, though not exclusive to this transethnic Celtic spirituality include penitence, pilgrimage, poetry, praise, and passion; God's homeliness and presence in creation; blessing and lament; the Trinity. And Celts see hymns as a way of winging earthbound mortals into heaven. So, even when neither the words nor the music come from one of these six 'nations', earthed hymns that notably combine several of these features are included. Conversely, famous hymn writers from these six lands are excluded if they are prisoner to one of the separated strands which are neither holistic nor rooted; as are many of the current glut of worship songs that cash in on the revival of interest in the 'Celtic' label but which divorce Jesus from the Trinity, justice from faith and people from the web of life.

What is Celtic music?

The lilt of Irish tunes, the syncopation of Scottish ballads, the fire and flow of Welsh community songs may all be recognised in this selection. Celtic music tends to be modal: in ancient times there were various modes, or scales, each with five notes. There is a preference for the pentatonic scale. The Lament and the Anthem are distinctive features: Anthems are a strong call to battle. Typical Celtic instruments include pipes, fiddles, bodhrán, whistle, strings and harp. Such instruments were common among ancient peoples who were in touch with primal drives. Both the bagpipe and the harp are mentioned in the Book of Daniel (3:7). Such instruments link us with the elements: human breath is linked to the breath of God; the vibrating harp strings pluck both the air and the heart. Such instruments are an enrichment, but the hymns in this book may be sung without them.

The Celtic vision is that we join as one in 'the song of all creation'. The world calls us to develop an intimate relationship between the body (lips, throat, lungs) and the spirit (breath). Singing helps to bring this about. Hildegaard of Bingen observed that *singing* words reveals their true meaning directly to the soul through bodily vibrations.

In the last quarter of the second millennium music developed on the Scottish Borders which put the Psalms into metrical verse and hymns into a common metre. Thus it is possible to put 'The Lord's My Shepherd' to any number of tunes from the ballads.

Songs of praise and what else?

In addition to its many songs of praise this book introduces songs of lament, blessing, celebration, and marching.

Lament

Voices from various lands have been calling for the church to include lamentation in its worship. Apart from Christ's Reproaches to his people on Good Friday there is little more than routine confessions in them. A New Zealander wrote of what was for her a strange experience on Good Friday: 'We were given the opportunity to approach the Cross in any way we chose to pray, etc. I felt neutral and unsure. But as I came to the Cross I suddenly found myself crouched down at its foot, one hand grasping the base tightly and the other shielding my face as I heaved with grief. Part of me was appalled – but it was so strong, coming from deep within me . . .'

Lamentation needs music, poetry, repetition – and time.

Blessing

Celtic Christianity teaches us to frequently bless people, places and things. These blessings are sometimes said, and at other times sung. St Patrick blessed Munster:

Blessing from the Lord on high
Over Munster fall and lie;

To her sons and daughters all
Choicest blessing still befall;
Fruitful blessing on the soil
That supports her faithful toil.

St Columba blessed bad fruit trees, a milking pail, cows, salt, journeys, households and places.

Blessings seem to have been prominent in the worship of early Celtic churches. The Antiphonary of Bangor, which may be the earliest surviving material from the worship of an Irish monastery, gives a central place to the *Benedicite*, the ancient Jewish hymn which calls on the elements of creation to bless the Lord. Some authorities claim that a characteristic of early Celtic Eucharists was frequent episcopal blessings during the course of the service (Ian Bradley *Colonies of Heaven*, Darton, Longman & Todd, page 59).

Blessing has been a feature of the Celtic spiritual tradition ever since, whether in the Welsh tradition of praise poems, in the Gaelic prayers of Scotland as evidenced in Alexander Carmichael's collection *The Carmina Gadelica* or in this hymn book.

In the early Christian centuries in Celtic lands it was normal to sing lullabies, for example, to an infant. These were probably songs of protection against harm as well as for soothing. Prayers and songs of protection and circling may be linked with blessing, and also with cursing, or, in Jesus' words, 'binding' (Matthew). Blessings communicated a powerful sense of God's goodness on what was blessed, and healing sometimes flowed from them.

Refrains
Hebrew pilgrimage songs make frequent use of refrains that are constantly repeated by the people as they draw near to the temple or shrine. Psalm 136 is an example of this. Such refrains are typical of African worship songs. The Celtic tradition restores this habit to western worship. The refrains may be used for penitence, praise, proclamation or intercession.

God's celebrities
The biblical habit of recalling (in the peoples' worship songs) God's hand in their story is also reviving among us through the Celtic renewal. Just as the psalms reverberate with references to God-guided personalities such as Abraham, Moses, Deborah and David, so this book reverberates with references to the likes of Patrick, Brigid, Aidan and Hilda. The cult of celebrities-apart-from-God flourishes in our culture. It is time our hymn books made room for God's celebrities.

Glimpses from the early Celtic church

Worship in the fifth-eighth century monastic churches was in Latin, which was then the main living language of educated people. Outside the monasteries worship was informal and in the language spoken by the general population. Almost nothing has been recorded of this. We do know that members of monastic churches went out to the villages taking with them a Gospel and a portable altar. They often gathered round a high, four-sided preaching Cross whose carvings illustrated Bible stories.

Columba's crowd sang their regular worship songs outside a ruler's head-quarters, as his biographer Adamnan describes:

When the saint himself was chanting the evening hymns with a few of the brothers, as usual, outside the king's fortification, some Druids did all they could to prevent God's praises being sung in the middle of a pagan nation. On seeing this, the saint began to sing the 44th Psalm, and at the same moment so wonderfully loud, like pealing thunder, did his voice become, that king and people were struck with awe (Adamnan, *Life of Saint Columba* [Penguin Books 1995]).

A ninth century text says Columba (d. 597) had a carrying voice heard at 1500 paces and it was like a melodious lion.

The early hymnology of the Irish monastic churches is known to us chiefly though two collections which have been published under the title *Irish Liber Hymnorum*. Columba's biographer Adamnan speaks of three hundred hymns written in Columba's own hand, some of them, it is thought, in Irish, a few of which have come down to us.

The *Life* of Columbanus (d. 615) reveals that priests wandered around with their harps, which were the guitars of those days, and we know that groups of Christians on a journey would welcome wandering bards to strum and sing along with them.

It seems there was not a big divide between worship and social gatherings. Bede's story of the seventh-century cowherd, Caedmon of Whitby, describes a large social gathering in the biggest barn in the area to which all the locals were invited. A musical instrument was passed around and each person had a turn at playing, singing or reciting poetry. It was hosted by the Christian monastic church; everyone (except Caedmon!) felt at home, and songs on any subject were shared.

The monastic churches had a routine framework of Psalms, canticles, prayers, creeds, responses and Bible readings which varied according to season. Some churches were dedicated to excellence in worship and set aside teams of worship leaders and musicians who offered the very best through the nights and days. Comgall's great monastic church at Bangor became known as The Valley of Angels. This was because over 3000 monks devoted themselves to the singing of Perennial Praise, based on the form of worship in the Tabernacle of King David as preserved by the Qumran Community in the deserts of Palestine. Thus the place later became known as Bangor Mor, The Great High Choir. Their praise book, the *Antiphonary of Bangor* is a collection of canticles, hymns, antiphons and versicles. There are fragments from the *Irish Books of Deer, Dimma and Mulling,* and from the *Sacramentaries of Gellone, Hildoard, Padua, Rheinau, Vellona.* This praise book, which is preserved in the Ambrosian Library, Milan, says 'Let the many keep awake in community on a third of the nights in the year in order to read aloud from the Book and to expound judgement and to sing blessings all together'.

Columbanus' monks sang a boat song as they rowed up the Rhine:

> Hold fast! Survive! And all is well,
> God sent you worse, He'll calm this swell.
> Heave, lads and let the echoes ring.

For many centuries prayers were said or sung as fishers and sailors set out on journeys. Today football and rugby songs are sung as fans travel to and from matches. We include a boat song which may be adapted for other forms of travel or work: 'Be our lives blest'.

Gaelic-speaking people seem to have used a wide variety of singing techniques. *Cormac's Glossary* (eighth/ninth century) and *The Book of Lismore* (compiled in the fifteenth century) mention these:

> Murmuring (Dord – murmuring; Dordan – light murmuring
> and Fodhord – low murmuring)
> Martial chants (Dord-fiansa)
> Purring sounds produced in the throat (Cronan)
> Song (Abram)
> Whistling (Fead)
> Melody (Duchand)
> Funeral cry (Logaireacht)
> Chorus (Cepoc)
> Chanting round fires, etc. (Esnad)

In Kilmartin Heritage Centre, near the site where St Columba first anointed a British monarch, the Scottish musicologist John Pursor has 'reconstructed' what he surmises might be a very ancient way of chanting from pre- and early-Christian times. It consists of long, elongated notes from deep down in the male larynx. Thus the human breath resonates with the echoes of a cave or waves; it is a primal experience. Perhaps liturgical chanting by an Orthodox priest, or even the chanting of Psalms in Gaelic by 'Wee Free' Churches in Scotland's Western Isles retain something of this. *The Inchcolm Antiphoner* (from the monastery, remains of which are on the islet of Inchcolm in the Firth of Forth) has hints of this, too.

The Plygain tradition in rural North and mid-Wales stretches back over four centuries. The Plygain is an early morning service held before dawn during Advent and Christmas time. It is largely lay led, when groups may sing carols, often very long and full of wonder, extolling the birth, life and death of Jesus. Several carols from this tradition are included in English translation.

Passion, presence and poetry.
Even if we had sufficient records, few, if any, would argue that we should copy the external forms of early Celtic worship. A more worthwhile question to address is 'What did they bring to worship?'

We know from the *Lives* of various saints that Celtic Christians tend to worship God with the whole of their being. We learn from Bede, for example, that when Cuthbert celebrated 'the Saving Victim' (the Holy Communion) he shed tears from the heart. We learn of a group of young monks who were so keen to keep up a ceaseless round of praise that they asked permission to sing Psalm 119, the longest Psalm by far, seven times each day! Most worshippers had no books. They said prayers and festal shouts from the gut. John O'Donohue, author of *Anam Cara: Spiritual Wisdom from the Celtic World,* writes of 'the music of one's own blood'. Please God, some of that music flows here.

In both Welsh and Gaelic the words for music and poetry are the same. St Paul described them as 'God's poem'. This hymn book, please God, breathes something of that spirit! It is offered as 'God's poem'. It is typical of Celtic poetry to repeat the last line: instead of rushing on from one thing to another, we savour the meaning of one thing at a time, and imbibe God's presence mediated through it. Songs can also help us cross the boundaries between earth and heaven.

When I asked a Scottish folk singer and minister what I should look for in a collection of Celtic hymns, he said, 'There is a certain something which you can't put your finger on.' I trust that 'certain something' will come out in this worship book as yeast comes out in bread.

CELTIC
HYMN BOOK

1 Adam, where are you

Michael Forster

Traditional Irish melody
arr. Keith Duke

SLANE 10 11 11 12

1. A-dam, where are you and why do you hide? You see the re-sult of in-dulg-ing your pride: you live in the sha-dows, and trem-ble with shame, sus-pi-cious and fear-ful to res-pond to your name.

2. Adam, where are you? The world is in pain,
   exploited and wounded for profit and gain,
   deprived of resources, polluted by greed,
   endangered by malice and neglected in need.

3. Adam, where are you? Face up to the truth,
   O leave not creation to die in her youth.
   God formed you from dust in the womb of the earth,
   so love and respect her who has given you birth.

4. Adam, where are you? Come into the light,
   though judgement is near yet the promise is bright,
   for hope in the darkness continues to gleam:
   God walks in the garden with the pow'r to redeem.

5. Adam, where are you? Come answer the call;
   the hope of redemption comes after the fall.
   The Spirit of wholeness, where chaos is rife,
   is calling creation to renewal and life!

2 Aidan and Oswald, King
A litany of Northumbrian Saints

Anthony Duncan

Martin Shaw
arr. Keith Duke

LITTLE CORNARD 66 66 and Refrain

1. Ai - dan and Os - wald, King, Fi - nan and Col - man too; Hil - da, En - fle - da, sing! Bede and Bar - tho - le - mew. At prayers of Nor - thern Saints, we pray: save and de - fend us, Lord, this day. day.

2. Henry of Coquet, pray;
   Edbert and Robert, call;
   Cuthbert and Wilfred, stay;
   hermits of Warkworth, all!

3. Oswin and Josephine,
   John and Paulinus true;
   you of the Church unseen,
   pray as we pray with you!

4. Peter and John and Paul,
   who in his steps have trod;
   Michael and angels all,
   Mother of Christ our God;

3 Alleluia (Celtic)

From the Liturgy

Fintan O'Carroll

CELTIC
HYMN BOOK

4 Alleluia (Iona)

From the Liturgy

Iona Community

5 All glory to God

Margaret Harvey
based on the *Gloria*

Traditional Welsh melody
arr. Keith Duke

THE ASH GROVE 12 11 12 11 D

1. All glo-ry to God in the heights of the hea-vens, and
peace to his peo-ple, his peo-ple on earth; we
praise you, we bless you, we give you our wor-ship, and
for your great glo-ry we sing out our thanks; O

2. Lord, you take away all the sin of the world, hear
   our prayer from your place at the Father's right hand;
   have mercy upon us; you only are holy
   and you, you alone, are our Lord and our God.
   Lord Christ, Holy Spirit and Father Almighty,
   Most High and most glorious, we give you our praise.
   All glory to God in the heights of the heavens,
   and peace to his people, his people on earth.

6 All glory to God who in mercy and grace

Ray Simpson

Traditional French melody
arr. Keith Duke

LOURDES 65 65 and Refrain

1. All glo-ry to God who, in mer-cy and grace, has fos-tered a home in this pil-grim-age place. Praise God! Praise God! Praise you for your saints! Praise God! Praise God! Praise you for your saints!

2. Remember Saint Patrick who lit up Christ's fire
   and rid Ireland's soil of its evils most dire.

3. Sing praises for Brigid, the midwife of Christ,
   who multiplied blessings with milled flour and yeast.

4. And Ninian the radiant who sighted the blind
   and built up the bright house whence multitudes wend.

5. When Illtyd ceased fighting and started a school,
   the young of the land flocked to learn of Christ's rule.

6. And David and Dyfrig and Samson and Paul
   there learned holy wisdom and took it to Gaul.

7. From Ireland Columba sailed over the sea
   and built on Iona a large monast'ry.

8. Northumbria's Oswald there grew in the faith
   then turned his raw kingdom into the Lord's base.

9. For Aidan the gentle brought faith to a land:
   transformed the rough English to Christ's faithful band.

10. A line of great Christians like Cuthbert appeared
    who healed many people whom once they had feared.

11. Like Hilda, the teacher of wisdom to all,
    who mentored the many and shone like a jewel.

12. When tyrants in Europe had turned a dark page
    these saints changed it into a new Golden Age.

13. We thank you, O Lord, for the saints of this place
    for ordinary folk who still fill it with grace.

14. All glory to God who, in mercy and grace,
    has fostered a home in this pilgrimage place.

7 All hail and welcome, holy child

Aodh MacCathmhaoil
trans. George Otto Simms

Traditional Irish melody
arr. Keith Duke

LUINNEACH Irregular
(♩. = 104)

1. All hail and wel - come, ho - ly child, you poor babe in the man - ger. So hap - py and rich it is you are to - night in - side your cas - tle.

2. God bless you, Jesus, once again!
Your life in its young body,
your face more lovely than the sun –
a thousand welcomes, baby!

3. Tonight we greet you in the flesh;
my heart adores my young king.
You came to us in human form –
I bring you a kiss and a greeting.

8 A mother dreamed

Ray Simpson

Traditional Somerset melody
arr. Keith Duke

O WALY WALY 88 88

1. A mo-ther dreamed her child un - born would shine like jew - els blaz-ing bright. From Eng-land's womb Hild leapt to life and bathed the land in Christ's own light.

2. She fostered gifts in timid folk,
   first English poet brought to flow'r
   whose songs sped round the people's haunts
   far from the corridors of power.

3. She mentored women called by God,
   Elfleda, *Heui and Bega too;
   she taught her priests to live a life
   which to their God the people drew.

4. Though sorely tried in mind and frame,
   she never ceased to give God praise;
   by night and day she faithful was,
   thus Hilda speaks to us always.

* Pronounced: *Hew*

CELTIC
HYMN BOOK

9 A new song sing to God

Colin Hodgetts
based on Psalm 98

Colin Hodgetts

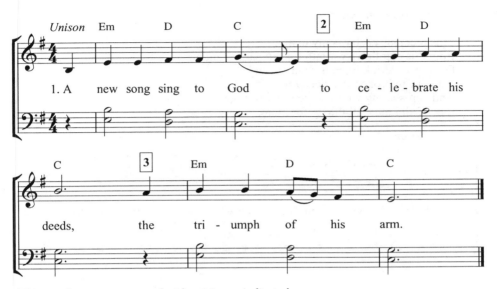

1. A new song sing to God to ce - le - brate his deeds, the tri - umph of his arm.

This may be sung as a round with entries as indicated.

2. His constancy and love
for children of his choice
are ever on his mind.

3. The near and distant lands
were privileged to see
the pow'r of God to save.

4. Let ev'ryone on earth
acclaim the Lord in song,
break into songs of joy.

5. With harp and voice praise God;
with trumpet, horn and drum
acclaim the Lord, the King.

6. Let sea and fishes roar,
let earth and people roar;
roar out with thund'rous voice.

7. Let rivers clap their hands
and mountains shout for joy
to greet the coming Lord.

8. He comes to rule the world,
to justly judge the earth;
with justice he will rule.

10 An invitation goes to all

Sammy Horner
Ray Simpson

Sammy Horner
arr. Keith Duke

Optional spoken introduction:

This precious nectar is my delight,
from this cup flows warmth for my darkest night.
From you I drink in, poise and power
though I'm broken in a needy hour.
And cup-sharing with me are rich and poor,
folk of all kinds, all thirsty for more.

1. An in-vi-ta-tion goes to all who lis-ten to their mas-ter's call, a
chair is al-ways wait-ing at his ta-ble. The
tired and wea-ry ga-ther in, you're wel-come if you're stained by sin, he'll
e-ven give you help if you aren't a-ble. This

2. So don't think that you can't partake,
   because your heart's about to break
   through all the tender snares that strip and cleave us.
   Though Christ was not the guilty one
   he saw the things that we had done
   and so he gave his life so he could save us.
   Yet none this way can save but Christ the King,
   it's so you only have yourself to bring.

11 As we think of our lifetime

Sammy Horner

Sammy Horner

1. As we think of our life-time and all that we've done, as we speak of the sto-ries of old; as we think of the past, and all that's gone by, when we've been both fear-ful and bold. Well I know that a life-time is bit-ter and sweet, and I

know that there's bo - ther and trou - ble to meet; and un -
til I'm in hea - ven that won't pass me by, and there'll
be not a tear in my eye.

2. As we think of the future and all it might bring,
   as we think what tomorrow may hold;
   as we pray for a place for our children to play,
   and for shelter when all us is cold.

CELTIC
HYMN BOOK

12 Awaken me, Lord

David Adam

Angela Reith

1. A - wak-en me, Lord, to your light: o - pen my eyes to your pre - sence.

2. Awaken me, Lord, to your love:
   open my heart to your indwelling.

3. Awaken me, Lord, to your life:
   open my mind to your abiding.

4. Awaken me, Lord, to your purpose:
   open my will to your guiding.

13 Behold, I see the virgin

Briege O'Hare

Briege O'Hare
arr. Keith Duke

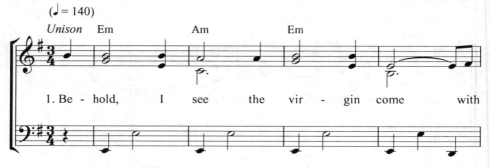

1. Be - hold, I see the vir - gin come with

Christ so young at her breast; the an - gels

bow - ing low be - fore, the Son of God at

rest. The vir - gin looks so glo - ri -

ous and Je - sus gleams like the snow;

she, like the moon in the hills a - ris - ing, and

he, like the sun a - glow.

2. O Mary, welcome to this house
   and welcome to your Son.
   O welcome, Holy Trinity,
   and welcome, Three in One.

CELTIC
HYMN BOOK

14 Behold the Lamb of God

John 1: 29

John L. Bell

Unhurried

Be - hold the Lamb of God, be - hold the Lamb of God who

Be - hold the Lamb, the Lamb of God who

takes a-way the sin, the sin of the world.

takes a - way the sin of the world.

15 Being of Life, being of Peace

Briege O'Hare

Briege O'Hare
arr. Keith Duke

1. Be - ing of Life, be - ing of

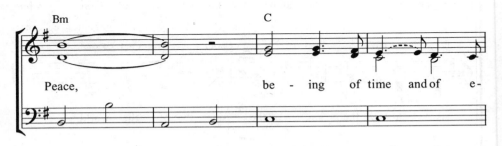

Peace, be - ing of time and of e-

ter - ni-ty.   Be - ing of Truth,

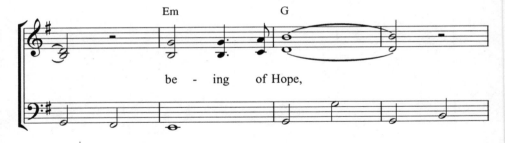

be - ing of Hope,

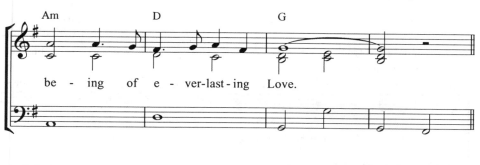

be - ing   of   e - ver-last-ing   Love.

Refrain

Bless me   in   my bo - dy,   bless me   in   my soul,

bless me   in   my com - ing and my   go   -   ing.

2. Being of earth, being of sky,
   being of seas and of rivers.
   Being of heart, being of soul,
   being of everlasting Love.

16 Be Jesus in my heart

Traditional Gaelic

Traditional Gaelic
arr. Keith Duke

17 Be our lives blessed

David Adam

Jacynth Hamill
arr. Keith Duke

2. *Cantor:* What shall we fear?
   All: What shall we fear, with God the Father near?
   What shall we fear, with God the Son near?
   What shall we fear, with God the Spirit near?
   What shall we fear, with God the Trinity near?

3. *Cantor:* Nothing shall we fear!
   All: Nothing shall we fear, with God the Father near!
   Nothing shall we fear, with God the Son near!
   Nothing shall we fear, with God the Spirit near!
   Nothing shall we fear, with God the Trinity near!

CELTIC
HYMN BOOK

18 Be still, for the presence of the Lord

David J. Evans   David J. Evans

1. Be still, for the pre-sence of the Lord, the Ho-ly One, is here.
Come, bow be-fore him now, with re-ve-rence and fear.
In him no sin is found, we stand on ho-ly ground.
Be still, for the pre-sence of the Lord, the Ho-ly One, is here.

2. Be still, for the glory of the Lord is shining all around;
he burns with holy fire, with splendour he is crowned.
How awesome is the sight, our radiant King of light!
Be still, for the glory of the Lord is shining all around.

3. Be still, for the power of the Lord is moving in this place;
he comes to cleanse and heal, to minister his grace.
No work too hard for him, in faith receive from him.
Be still, for the power of the Lord is moving in this place.

19 Be the strength of God

God between

David Adam

Rosemary Turnbull
arr. Keith Duke

Be the strength of God bet-ween me and each weak - ness;

be the light of God bet-ween me and each dark - ness.

Be the joy of God bet-ween me and each sad - ness;

be the calm of God bet-ween me and each mad - ness.

CELTIC
HYMN BOOK

20 Be thou a smooth way

Carmina Gadelica

Traditional Scottish melody
arr. Keith Duke

Be thou a smooth way be - fore us, be thou a guid-ing star a-bove us, be thou a keen eye be-hind us, this day, this night and for e - ver.

21 Be thou my vision

Irish (c.8th century)
trans. Mary Byrne and Eleanor Hull

Traditional Irish melody
arr. Keith Duke

SLANE 10 10 10 10

(♩ = 92)

1. Be thou my vis-ion, O Lord of my heart, naught be all else to me save that thou art; thou my best thought in the day and the night, wak-ing or sleep-ing, thy pres-ence my light.

2. Be thou my wisdom, be thou my true word,
   I ever with thee and thou with me, Lord;
   thou my great Father, and I thy true heir;
   thou in me dwelling, and I in thy care.

3. Be thou my breastplate, my sword for the fight,
   be thou my armour, and be thou my might,
   thou my soul's shelter, and thou my high tow'r,
   raise thou me heav'nward, O Pow'r of my pow'r.

4. Riches I need not, nor all the world's praise,
   thou mine inheritance through all my days;
   thou, and thou only, the first in my heart,
   high King of heaven, my treasure thou art!

5. High King of heaven, when battle is done,
   grant heaven's joy to me, O bright heav'n's sun;
   Christ of my own heart, whatever befall,
   still be my vision, O Ruler of all.

22 Blessed Hilda

Ray Simpson

Henry Purcell
arr. Keith Duke

WESTMINSTER ABBEY 87 87 87

(♩ = 132)

1. Bles - sed Hil - da, ho - ly mo - ther, friend of Ai - dan,

Christ's own stalk; born to ho - nour, stripped of fa - ther,

find - ing faith, bap - tised at York; shin - ing as a

ra - diant jew - el, light - ing up our dark - ened walk.

2. Taught of God by Wearside river,
   daring, learning, steeped in prayer;
   you became a guide to many,
   friend of people far and near;
   drawing out the cowherd's talents,
   held by earth and heav'n most dear.

3. Faithful host and reconciler,
   staying true through shifting ties;
   thankful in success and trial,
   always fair and always wise;
   meditator, motivator,
   wisdom's gem, and heaven's prize.

23 Bless to me, O God

Briege O'Hare
based on Carmina Gadelica

Briege O'Hare
arr. Keith Duke

Bless to me, O God, the earth be-neath my feet,
bless to me, O God, the path where-on I go,
bless to me, O God, the thing of my de-sire. Thou
e - ver-more of e - ver-more, bless to me my rest.

2. Bless to me the thing whereon is set my mind,
   bless to me the thing whereon is set my love,
   bless to me the thing whereon is set my hope.

24 Bread is blessed and broken

John L. Bell
Graham Maule

John L. Bell

GRACE IN ESSENCE 65 63

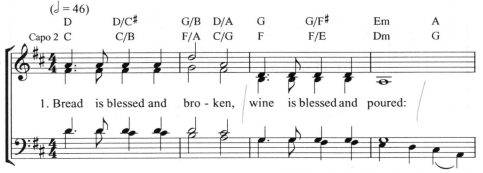

Bread is blessed and bro-ken, wine is blessed and poured:
(Basses) is blessed, is blessed and poured:

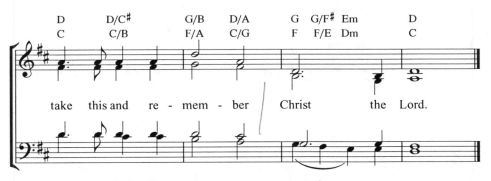

take this and re-mem-ber Christ the Lord.

This hymn is particularly effective when sung unaccompanied

2. Share the food of heaven
   earth cannot afford.
   Here is grace in essence –
   Christ the Lord.

3. Know yourself forgiven,
   find yourself restored,
   meet a friend for ever –
   Christ the Lord.

4. God has kept his promise
   sealed by sign and word:
   here, for those who want him –
   Christ the Lord.

25 Calm me, Lord

David Adam

Margaret Rizza

Tranquil (♩ = 108)

Calm me, Lord, as you calmed the storm; still me, Lord, keep me from harm. Let all the tu-mult with-in me cease; en-fold me, Lord, in your peace. Lord, en-fold me in your peace.

To repeat ad lib.

Last time

Text © Copyright SPCK, Holy Trinity Church, Marylebone Road, London NW1 4DU.
Used by permission from *The Edge of Glory*.
Music © Copyright 1998 Kevin Mayhew Ltd.

26 Child in the manger

Mary MacDonald
trans. Lachlan MacBean

Keith Duke

KIRKMADRINE 55 53 D

1. Child in the manger, infant of Mary;
out-cast and stranger, Lord of all;
child who in-he-rits all our trans-gres-sions,
all our de-me-rits on him fall.

2. Once the most holy child of salvation
gently and lowly lived below;
now as our glorious mighty Redeemer,
see him victorious o'er each foe.

3. Prophets foretold him, infant of wonder;
angels behold him on his throne;
worthy our Saviour of all their praises;
happy for ever are his own.

27 Christ as a light

Ray Simpson

Sarah Watts

SHRIMPFISHERS 10 9 D

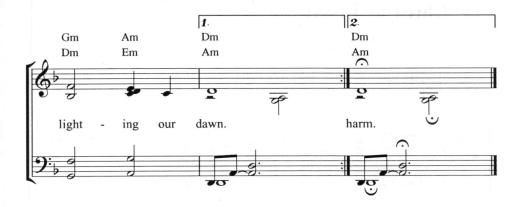

light - ing our dawn. harm.

2. Christ in the lonely, Christ in the hungry,
Christ in the sleepless, Christ in the worn;
Christ as a light illumine and guide them,
Christ as a shield protect them from harm.

28 Christ be beside me

St Patrick's Breastplate
adapted by James Quinn

Traditional Gaelic melody
arr. Keith Duke

BUNESSAN 55 54 D

1. Christ be be-side me, Christ be be-fore me, Christ be be-hind me, King of my heart; Christ be with-in me, Christ be be-low me, Christ be a-bove me, ne-ver to part.

2. Christ on my right hand, Christ on my left hand,
   Christ all around me, shield in the strife.
   Christ in my sleeping, Christ in my sitting,
   Christ in my rising, light of my life.

3. Christ be in all hearts thinking about me.
   Christ be in all tongues telling of me.
   Christ be the vision in eyes that see me,
   in ears that hear me, Christ ever be.

29 Christ be near at either hand

David Adam

Keith Duke

1. Christ be near at ei-ther hand, Christ be-hind, be-fore me

stand, Christ with me wher-e'er I go, Christ a-

round, a-bove, be - low. Christ be end.

2. Christ be in my heart and mind,
   Christ within my soul enshrined,
   Christ control my wayward heart,
   Christ abide and ne'er depart.

3. Christ my life and only way,
   Christ my lantern night and day,
   Christ be my unchanging friend,
   Guide and Shepherd to the end.

CELTIC
HYMN BOOK

30 Christ be with me

Ascribed to St Patrick
trans. Cecil Frances Alexander

Noel Rawsthorne
based on Johann Pachelbel's
Canon in D, arr. Keith Duke

1. Christ be with me, Christ with-in me, Christ be-hind me, Christ be-fore me, Christ be-side me, Christ to guide me, Christ to com-fort and re-store me.

2. Christ beneath me, Christ above me,
   Christ in quiet, Christ in danger,
   Christ in hearts of all that love me,
   Christ in care of friend and stranger.

31 Circle me, Lord

David Adam   Keith Duke

TUNE 1

1. Cir - cle me, Lord, keep pro - tec - tion near, and dan - ger far.

2. Cir - cle me, Lord, keep hope with - in, keep doubt with - out.

3. Cir - cle me, Lord, keep light

Sing the four lines of the round in unison (or as a solo),
then sing it as a round once or twice;
then move on to the coda without a break,
singing it as many times as necessary.

David Adam

Traditional Irish melody
arr. Keith Duke

TUNE 2: MAIRE RUA 13 12 12 12

(♩. = 60)

32 Circle me now, O God of life

Ray Simpson

John Michael Talbot

2. Circle me now, O God of life;
   circle me now, O God.
   Keep in the things that make me true;
   keep in the good that grows.
   Circle me now, O God of life;
   circle me now, O God.

33 Cloth for the cradle

John L. Bell
Graham Maule

Traditional Scottish melody
arr. Keith Duke

WAE'S FOR ME PRINCE CHARLIE Irregular and Refrain

($\quad$ = 100)

Cloth for the cra - dle, cra - dle for the child, the child for our ev - 'ry joy and sor - row; find him a shawl that's wo - ven by us all to wel - come the Lord of all to - mor - row.

2. Claimant and queen, wage earners in between,
   trader and travelling preacher,
   weave into one a welcome for the Son,
   whose word brings new life to ev'ry creature.

3. Hungry and poor, the sick and the unsure,
   wealthy, whose needs are stranger,
   weave into one a welcome for the Son,
   leave excess and want beneath the manger.

4. Wrinkled or fair, carefree or full of care,
   searchers of all the ages,
   weave into one a welcome for the Son,
   the Saviour of shepherds and of sages.

34 Come and find the quiet centre

Shirley Erena Murray

Attributed to B.F. White from
The Sacred Harp (1844)
arr. Keith Duke

BEACH SPRING 87 87 D

1. Come and find the qui-et cen - tre in the crowd - ed life we lead, find the room for hope to en - ter find the frame where we are freed: clear the cha - os and the clut - ter, clear our eyes, that we can see all the things that real-ly mat - ter, be at peace, and simp-ly be.

2. Silence is a friend who claims us,
   cools the heat and slows the pace,
   God it is who speaks and names us,
   knows our being, touches base,
   making space within our thinking,
   lifting shades to show the sun,
   raising courage when we're shrinking,
   finding scope for faith begun.

3. In the Spirit let us travel,
   open to each other's pain,
   let our loves and fears unravel,
   celebrate the space we gain:
   there's a place for deepest dreaming,
   there's a time for heart to care,
   in the Spirit's lively scheming
   there is always room to spare!

CELTIC
HYMN BOOK

35 Come, Creator Spirit

Ray Simpson

Keith Duke

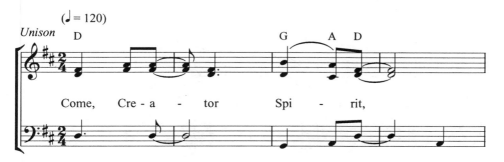

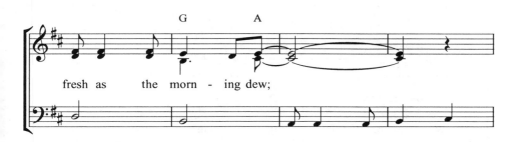

36 Come, Lord Jesus

Maranatha

David Adam

Keith Duke

Response:
Come, Lord Jesus.

Solo:
1. When this world's as dark as night;
2. When we are tempted to go astray;
3. When we are falling in the strife;
4. When troubles to our lives bring harm;
5. When the storms of life increase;
6. When our lives are full of woe;
7. When we are down and all forlorn;

37 Come, my Lord, my light, my way

David Adam

Keith Duke

TUNE 1

($\quad$ = 112)

Unison

Come, my Lord, my light, my way;

come, my lan - tern night and day;

come, my heal - er, make me whole;

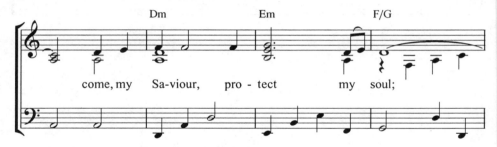

come, my Sa - viour, pro - tect my soul;

come, my King, enter my heart;

come, Prince of Peace, and ne - ver de - part.

David Adam

Rosemary Turnbull
arr. Keith Duke

TUNE 2

Come, my Lord, my light, my way, come my lan - tern,

night and day. Come my heal - er, make me whole,

come my Sa - viour pro - tect my soul. Come my King,

en - ter my heart; come Prince of Peace and ne - ver de - part.

38 Come to me

Rosemary Turnbull

Rosemary Turnbull
arr. Keith Duke

1. Come to me and I will give you life; your strength will
be re-newed to meet the strife. Come to me,
you have a choice to make, my arms to you are stretched,
rise up, a-wake. one.

2. Come to me, and I will with you go
   all through your daily walk, safe from the foe.
   Come to me, and tell me all your fears,
   and I will comfort you, your cry I hear.

3. Come to me, and I will dwell with you,
   no more you'll be alone, my word is true.
   Come to me, and when your time is come
   to join your heav'nly home, we will be one.

CELTIC
HYMN BOOK

39 Deep peace

Fiona McLeod

Norman Richardson
arr. Keith Duke

40 Deep peace of the running wave

Fiona McLeod

Keith Duke

Deep peace of the run-ning wave to you;

deep peace of the flow-ing air to you;

deep peace of the qui - et earth to you;

deep peace of the shin-ing stars to you;

deep   peace   of the Son   of   Peace   to   you;

deep   peace,   deep   peace.

CELTIC
HYMN BOOK

41 Deo gratias

From the Liturgy

John L. Bell

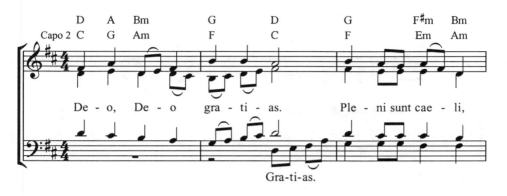

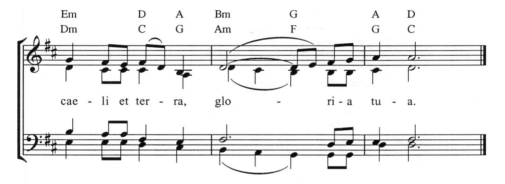

42 Does the flame burn brighter

Paul Kyle

Paul Kyle
arr. Keith Duke

Does the flame burn bright-er in your hand than it burned in the

hand of your fa - ther when he said, 'It's your turn, take the

torch of faith, run through - out the land, let the flame burn bright with -

in you.' When our fa - thers joined in that pil - grim band, they were

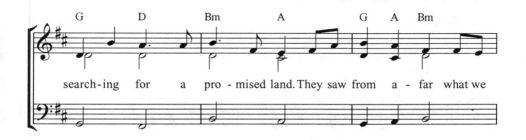

searching for a pro-mised land. They saw from a-far what we

know is near as the One who loved and bought us.

43 Ebb tide, full tide

Ray Simpson

Keith Duke

LINDISFARNE

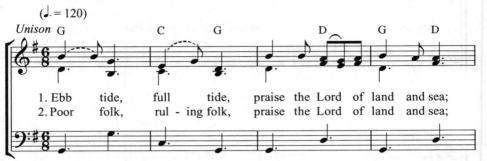

1. Ebb tide, full tide, praise the Lord of land and sea;
2. Poor folk, rul-ing folk, praise the Lord of land and sea;

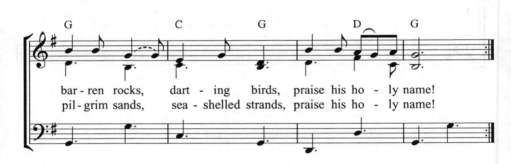

bar-ren rocks, dart-ing birds, praise his ho-ly name!
pil-grim sands, sea-shelled strands, praise his ho-ly name!

Refrain

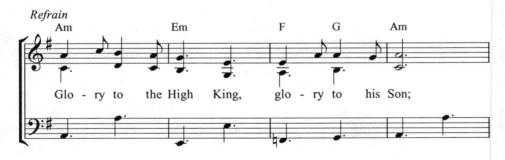

Glo-ry to the High King, glo-ry to his Son;

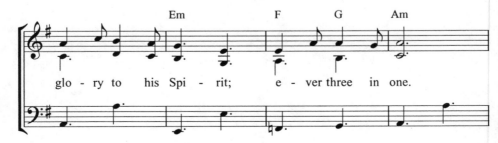

glo-ry to his Spi-rit; e-ver three in one.

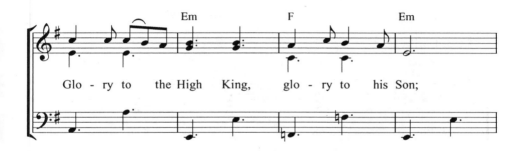

Glo - ry to the High King, glo - ry to his Son;

glo - ry to his Spi - rit, e - ver three in one.

3. Fierce lions, gentle lambs,
   praise the Lord of land and sea;
   noble women, mission priests,
   praise his holy name!

4. Chanting boys, slaves set free,
   praise the Lord of land and sea;
   old and young and all the land,
   praise his holy name!

44 Embrace the universe with love

June Boyce-Tillman

Irish melody from the *Petrie Collection*
arr. Keith Duke

ST COLUMBA 87 87

1. Em - brace the u - ni - verse with love, and

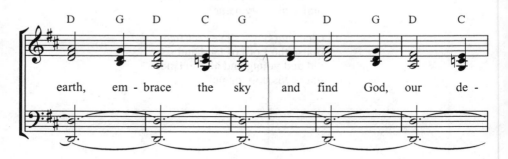

shine with God in splen - dour. Em - brace the

earth, em - brace the sky and find God, our de -

To next verse | Last time

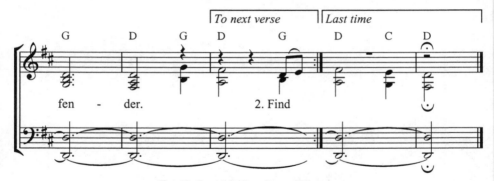

fen - der. 2. Find

2. Find wisdom hidden in the stars
   and faith within the rainbow;
   find righteousness in flowing streams
   and hope in moon and meadow.

3. Embrace your friend, embrace your foe
   and find the Christ within them;
   embrace your body and your mind;
   these also are God-given.

4. For mercy dwells in human hearts
   and needs our love to shape it.
   Put out a hand and touch a heart
   and help to consecrate it.

5. Share all you have with all you meet
   and find the strength of Scripture;
   prepare the heart, prepare the mind
   and leave to God the future.

6. So even death when joy is deep
   can be Christ's benediction.
   Creator-God, we sing your praise,
   like Hilda, seek your vision.

45 Empty, broken, here I stand

Kyrie eleison

Nick and Anita Haigh

Nick and Anita Haigh
arr. Keith Duke

2. When my faith has all but gone,
   Kyrie eleison,
   give me strength to carry on,
   Kyrie eleison.
   When my dreams have turned to dust,
   Kyrie eleison,
   in you, O Lord, I put my trust,
   Kyrie eleison.
   Kyrie . . .

3. When my heart is cold as ice,
   Kyrie eleison,
   your love speaks of sacrifice,
   Kyrie eleison.
   Love that sets the captive free,
   Kyrie eleison,
   O pour compassion down on me,
   Kyrie eleison.
   Kyrie . . .

4. You're the voice that calms my fears,
   Kyrie eleison,
   you're the laughter, dries my tears,
   Kyrie eleison.
   You're my music, my refrain,
   Kyrie eleison,
   help me sing your song again,
   Kyrie eleison.
   Kyrie . . .

5. Humble heart of holiness,
   Kyrie eleison,
   kiss me with your tenderness,
   Kyrie eleison.
   Jesus, faithful friend and true,
   Kyrie eleison,
   all I am I give to you,
   Kyrie eleison.
   Kyrie . . .

46 Ever-shielding Father

Ray Simpson

Keith Duke

CELTIC
HYMN BOOK

47 Father, give your love

Wedding Song

Trevor Thorn

Trevor Thorn
arr. Keith Duke

Fa-ther, give your love and build it in us your ser-vants,
guide us to share love ev - 'ry day;
cre - ate in each an af - fec-tion re - flect-ing your love,
gen-'rous be - yond the world's way.

2. Jesus, give your peace
   and grow it in us your servants,
   hold it in our homes ev'ry day;
   may it flow outwards
   to those we encounter
   as witness that peace is your way.

3. Spirit, give your joy
   and spread it through us your servants,
   help us be joyful ev'ry day;
   with love and peace, may
   our joy be in great abundance
   as we build life in your way.

48 For the fruits of your creation

Fred Pratt Green, alt.

Keith Duke

To next verse

Last time

earth's safe-keep-ing, thanks be to God! God!

2. In the just reward of labour,
   God's will is done;
   in the help we give our neighbour,
   God's will is done;
   in our worldwide task of caring
   for the hungry and despairing;
   in the harvests we are sharing,
   God's will is done.

3. For the harvests of the Spirit,
   thanks be to God!
   For the good we all inherit,
   thanks be to God!
   For the wonders that astound us,
   for the truths that still confound us;
   most of all, that love has found us,
   thanks be to God!

49 For yours is the kingdom

From the Liturgy

John L. Bell

50 From our hearts we pray

Ray Simpson

Traditional
arr. Keith Duke

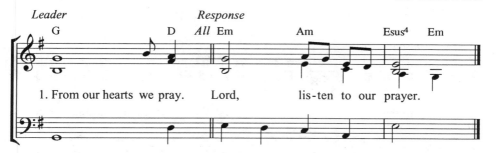

2. We offer to you all we are, all we have,
   and all we do this day, that you will be
   given the glory.

Response

3. We offer to you all whom we shall meet this day;
   give them the grace of eternal life.

Response

4. We offer to you our homes, schools, and places
   of work; may they be places of dignity, joy
   and simplicity.

Response

5. We offer you victims of prejudice, oppression and neglect;
   may everyone be cherished from conception to the grave.

Response

6. We offer to you the concerns on each of our hearts
   (all silently or aloud mention names or needs)

Response

51 From the falter of breath

John L. Bell
Graham Maule

Traditional Scottish melody
arr. Keith Duke

IONA BOAT SONG 66 9 D

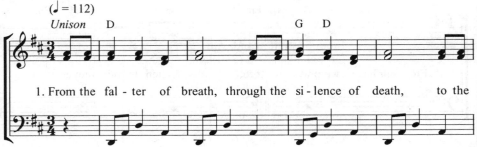

1. From the fal-ter of breath, through the si-lence of death, to the

won-der that's break-ing be-yond; God has

wo-ven a way, un-ap-pa-rent by day, for all

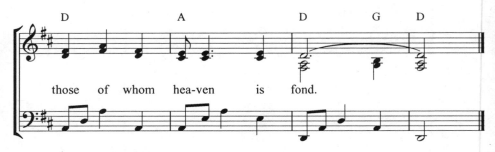

those of whom hea-ven is fond.

2. From frustration and pain,
   through hope hard to sustain,
   to the wholeness here promised, there known;
   Christ has gone where we fear
   and has vowed to be near
   on the journey we make on our own.

3. From the dimming of light,
   through the darkness of night,
   to the glory of goodness above;
   God the Spirit is sent
   to ensure heav'n's intent
   is embraced and completed in love.

4. From today till we die,
   through all questioning why,
   to the place from which time and tide flow;
   angels tread on our dreams
   and magnificent themes
   of heav'n's promise are echoed below.

CELTIC
HYMN BOOK

52 From your earth, Lord

Ray Simpson

Ray Simpson
arr. Keith Duke

From your earth, Lord, won-ders flow. One more won - der,
Lord; Lord, change my life.

53 Gather around, for the table is spread

Jean Holloway

Traditional Scottish melody
and Annie McLeod
arr. Keith Duke

SKYE BOAT SONG 10 6 10 6 86 86 10 6 10 6

($\downarrow$ = 120)

Ga - ther a - round, for the ta - ble is spread, wel - come the

food and rest! Wide is our cir - cle with

Christ at the head, he is the hon - oured guest.

Learn of his love, grow in his grace, pray for the

54 Give me a vision

David Adam

Keith Duke

55 Gloria

Iona Gloria

Traditional

Traditional
arr. Keith Duke

Glo - ri - a, glo - ri - a, glo - ri - a

in ex - cel - sis De - o.

CELTIC
HYMN BOOK

56 Glory to God

Incarnatus est

David Adam

Jacques Berthier

2. Glory to God, on earth peace,
   let this song never cease.
   When I wash my face,
   bless me with your grace.

3. Glory to God, on earth peace,
   let this song never cease.
   When I comb my hair,
   keep me from despair.

57 Glory to thee, O God of life

John Michael Talbot

John Michael Talbot
arr. Keith Duke

CELTIC
HYMN BOOK

58 Glory to the Father

Ray Simpson

Bede's Deathsong

Friedrich Filitz
arr. Keith Duke

CASWALL 65 65

1. Glo - ry to the Fa - ther, glo - ry to the Son,

glo - ry to the Spi - rit; e - ver Three - in - One.

2. Praise for those who mirrored
   triune Love on earth;
   shining in Bede's pages
   signs that life has worth.

3. Thank you for Bede's learning,
   for his ready pen,
   for a lifetime's labours
   crowned with heav'n's 'Amen!'

4. Kneeling at his dying,
   brothers at his side;
   chanting to his maker
   at Ascensiontide

5. Glory to the Father,
   glory to the Son,
   glory to the Spirit,
   ever Three-in-One.

59 God above, God below

Paul Neeley

Traditional Scottish melody
arr. Keith Duke

THE DARK ISLAND Irregular

(♩ = 88)

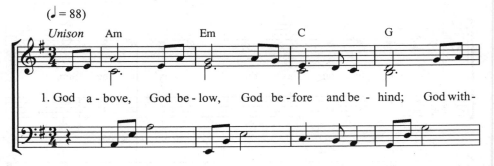

1. God a-bove, God be-low, God be-fore and be-hind; God with-

in all of my life, in my heart, in my mind. Mer-ci-

ful, migh-ty King, hea-ven's Son we will praise. God en-

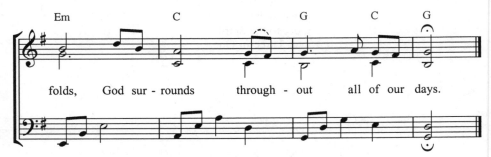

folds, God sur-rounds through-out all of our days.

2. May his glory shine forth as we kneel in this place;
   may his will be done always as we seek his face.
   May his kingdom now come, may we hear and obey;
   may we love Christ alone: purify us as we pray.

3. Be the bright sun to warm, be the star that will guide;
   be the smooth road before me, be the place that I can hide.
   Be the strength of my legs, be the start of my path;
   be the word in my mouth, be the deep joy in my laugh.

4. Be my thoughts, be my deeds, be my ebb and my flow;
   make me seed that is planted, you be wheat that will grow.
   Jesus Christ, Living Hope, Lord of sea and of sky
   be our health while we live, be our new life when we die.

5. Be my sword for the fight, be the goal of my quest;
   be my shield of protection, be the stream where I rest.
   Be the door that I seek, be the gold that I find;
   be all wisdom to me, be the filling of my mind.

6. God of earth, God of fire, God of water and wind;
   God who made the beginning, God who holds the end.
   Be the dawning of day, be the close of our eyes;
   be the blessing we seek, be the comfort to our cries.

7. Morning Star, Perfect Lamb, Risen King over death;
   Word of God, Son of Mary be our life, be our breath.
   Full of truth, full of grace, Holy God, wash us clean;
   King of kings, Precious One, fill us with your peace serene.

60 God be with my going out

Going and coming

David Adam

Norman Warren

1. God be with my go-ing out, God be with my com-ing in, God be with me in my doubt, God pro-tect-ing me from sin.

2. Christ be with my ebbing,
   Christ be with my flowing,
   Christ be with my ent'ring,
   Christ in love bestowing.

3. Spirit with me ev'ry hour,
   Spirit at the journey's end,
   Spirit be my ev'ry power,
   Spirit dove, on me descend.

61 God, bless to us our bodies

Ray Simpson

Keith Duke

62 God of freedom, God of justice

Shirley Erena Murray

Traditional Welsh melody
from *Musical Relicks of Welsh Bards*
arr. Keith Duke

RHUDDLAN 87 87 87

2. Rid the earth of torture's terror,
God whose hands were nailed to wood;
hear the cries of pain and protest,
God who shed the tears and blood;
move in us the pow'r of pity,
restless for the common good.

3. Make in us a captive conscience
quick to hear, to act, to plead;
make us truly sisters, brothers,
of whatever race or creed:
teach us to be fully human,
open to each other's need.

63 God of life be with you

David Adam

Angela Reith
arr. Keith Duke

64 God, our Creator

Stephen Eric Smyth

HIGHLAND CATHEDRAL 10 10 10 10 D

Traditional Scottish melody
arr. Keith Duke

1. God, our Cre-a-tor, hear us sing in praise.
We sing in praise for the great gifts you give:

God, al-ways ten-der, God who knows our ways.
all of cre-a-tion, ev-'ry-thing that lives,

God, al-ways pre-sent, God who real - ly cares.
glo - ries of na-ture, our own time on earth,

We of-fer thanks for all the love you share.
send - ing your Son a-mong us proves our worth.

Refrain

Loud is our praise as we sing of you, one with

peo - ple of faith, an - cient and new.

Bless us a - fresh with your grace, we pray. Help us

To next verse *Last time*

D.C.

wit - ness your love to - day. day.

2. Thanks for the blessings of the talents, skills,
   fam'lies and friendships by which lives are filled.
   Thanks for the graces, gifts you spread so wide:
   those that the world sees and those deep inside.
   Even in hard times we can praise your name.
   You're always with us, loving just the same.
   Sickness or sorrow, loneliness or doubt,
   help us remember your hand reaches out.

3. Gathered together, sisters, brothers all,
   baptised in Jesus, faithful to your call,
   we are one fam'ly. May your will be done
   and, for all people, may your Kingdom come.
   'God who is love', you are our Father true;
   Jesus, our brother, fully human too;
   Spirit, your presence, with us ev'ry day;
   love is your essence, love our truest way.

   Repeat verse 1

CELTIC
HYMN BOOK

65 God to enfold you

God enfolding

John L. Bell

John L. Bell

66 Gonna lay down my sword and shield

Down by the riverside

Spiritual

Spiritual
arr. Keith Duke

2. Gonna walk with the Prince of Peace . . .

3. Gonna shake hands around the world . . .

67 Good King Oswald

Anthony Duncan

Traditional Welsh melody
arr. Keith Duke

Good King Os - wald, glad re - turn - ing

from the fight at Hea - ven - field,

called for Ai - dan, wise, dis - cern - ing,

that his peo - ple might be healed,

and, in ho - li - ness and learn - ing,

find, in Christ, their King, and yield.

2. King and Bishop rode together,
   preached the Gospel side by side;
   taught the Faith 'mid rocks and heather,
   forests, fields and stormy tide,
   fire and flood and wind and weather;
   standing always side by side.

3. Pray for us! You Saints who founded
   this our Church in time long past.
   Pray for us! That we be grounded
   in true faith and hold it fast.
   Pray for us! That thus surrounded,
   we're found faithful at the last.

CELTIC
HYMN BOOK

68 Goodness is stronger than evil

Desmond Tutu

John L. Bell

GOODNESS IS STRONGER 86 76 85

69 Great God, you are the Father

St Columba
alt. Nick Fawcett

Traditional Irish melody
arr. Keith Duke

DURROW 76 76 D

($\quad$ = 120)

1. Great God, you are the Father of all who have believed: from
you the hosts of heaven have life and power received. O
God, you are the maker of all created things, the
righteous judge of judges, the almighty King of kings.

2. You reign enthroned in splendour
   our heavn'ly sov'reign Lord,
   and when Christ comes in glory
   your name will be adored.
   You shine beyond our knowing,
   the everlasting Light;
   ineffable in loving,
   unthinkable in might.

3. To those who humbly seek you
   your secrets you unfold;
   you are the root of all things,
   the source of new and old.
   I walk secure and blessèd
   wherever life may run,
   for you, O God, are with me,
   almighty, Three in One.

70 Guide me, O thou great Redeemer

William Williams
trans. Peter Williams

John Hughes

CWM RHONDDA 87 87 87 7

1. Guide me, O thou great Re-deem-er, pil-grim through this bar-ren land; I am weak, but thou art migh-ty, hold me with thy pow'r-ful hand: Bread of Hea-ven, Bread of Hea-ven, feed me till I want no

(want no more)
more, feed me till I want no more.

(want no more)

2. Open now the crystal fountain,
   whence the healing stream doth flow;
   let the fire and cloudy pillar
   lead me all my journey through;
   strong deliv'rer, strong deliv'rer,
   be thou still my strength and shield,
   be thou still my strength and shield.

3. When I tread the verge of Jordan,
   bid my anxious fears subside;
   death of death, and hell's destruction,
   land me safe on Canaan's side;
   songs of praises, songs of praises,
   I will ever give to thee,
   I will ever give to thee.

71 Hail the coming Prince of Peace

Hail the King

Paul Neeley

Sean Clarach MacDhomnaill
arr. Keith Duke

MOGHILLE MEAR 77 88 and Refrain

Hail the com-ing Prince of Peace, hail the Sa-viour of us all.

Hail the cho-sen Lamb of God, O crown him Lord for e - ver.

1. Here he comes our God and King, coats and bran-ches we will bring. He

rides up-on a don-key's back as loud ho-san-nas we do sing.

Hail the o-ver-com-ing King, hail the one who con-quered death.

Hail Re-deem-er of the world, O crown him Lord for e - ver.

2. He came the first time as a child,
   by lawless men he was reviled;
   he only sought his Father's will
   as he lived his whole life undefiled.

3. Soon he'll come upon the cloud;
   ev'ry knee will then be bowed.
   He'll take his rightful throne at last
   and all the earth will shout aloud.

72 Hear all creation

Margaret Becker

Keith Getty
arr. Keith Duke

1. Hear all cre-a-tion lift its voice, the moun-tains sing and the ri-vers re-joice for the name of Je-sus, for his name. And we, his peo-ple, saved by grace, we bow our heads and we bring our praise to the

2. He mends our hearts, he keeps our ways;
he lights our nights and he leads our days
all for his glory, for his name.
There's nothing greater than to be his,
to bring him glory and to fully live
for the name of Jesus, for his name.

73 Here be the peace

Ray Simpson
based on Aidan's *Prayer for Holy Island*

Traditional Irish melody
arr. Keith Duke

DANNY BOY 12 10 11 10 12 10 11 12

74 Here I stand at the door

Revelation 3:20

John L. Bell

Here I stand at the door and knock, and knock.

Here I stand at the door and knock, and

I will come and dine with those who ask me in.

knock. I will dine with those who ask me in.

75 Here, Lord, we take the broken bread

C.V. Pilcher

Irish melody from the *Petrie Collection*
arr. Keith Duke

ST COLUMBA 87 87

1. Here, Lord, we take the bro-ken bread and drink the wine be-liev - ing that by your life our souls are fed, your part - ing gifts re-ceiv - ing.

2. As

2. As you have giv'n, so we would give
   ourselves for others' healing;
   and as you lived, so we would live,
   the Father's love revealing.

CELTIC
HYMN BOOK

76 Holy God

From the Liturgy

Traditional
arr. Keith Duke

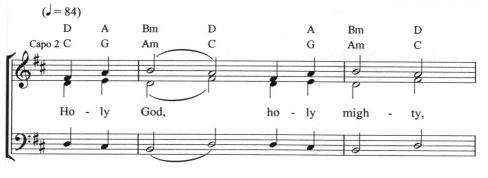

77 Holy, holy, holy Lord

Sanctus

From the Liturgy

Traditional Scottish melody
arr. Keith Duke

CELTIC
HYMN BOOK

78 Holy, most holy

Slane Sanctus

Michael Forster
based on the _Sanctus_

Traditional Irish melody
arr. Keith Duke

SLANE 10 11 11 11

2. Blessèd, most blessèd, all blessèd is he
   whose life makes us whole, and whose death sets us free:
   who comes in the name of the Father of light,
   let endless hosannas resound in the height.

79 Holy Weaver, may we watch you *Eternal treasure*

Martin E. Leckebusch

Andrew Wright

ETERNAL TREASURE 87 88 87

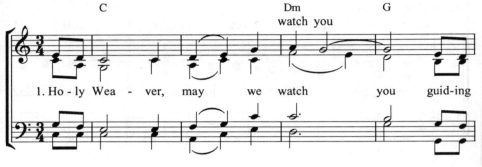

1. Ho-ly Wea - ver, may we watch you guid-ing

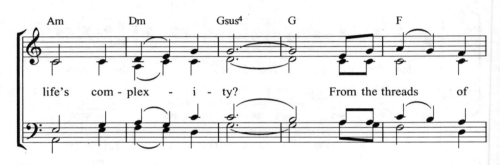

life's com - plex - i - ty? From the threads of

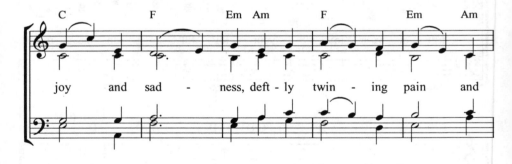

joy and sad - ness, deft - ly twin - ing pain and

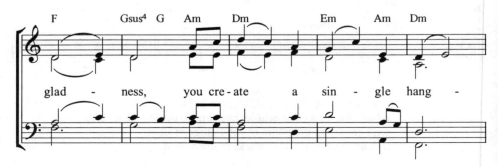

glad - ness, you cre - ate a sin - gle hang -

ing: one e - ter - nal   ta - pes - try.

2. We will listen, truthful Poet –
   listen to your words of grace:
   human cries of faith and passion,
   grief and hope, you take and fashion
   in the saga, yet unfolding,
   of your dealings with our race.

3. Skilful Artist, how we trust you,
   place our hope in you alone:
   on a canvas stained with sorrow
   you can paint a bright tomorrow
   and, with unimagined colours,
   make your sov'reign purpose known.

4. We adore you, mighty Goldsmith:
   all to you we gladly yield!
   Jeweller in eternal treasure,
   for your good and holy pleasure
   take our lives, refine and shape us
   till your glory is revealed.

80 How blessed are you

From *The Sermon on the Mount*

Jacques Berthier

81 How good it is to know your name

Damian Lundy

Traditional Breton melody
arr. Keith Duke

1. How good it is to know your name. You came to

claim us long a - go. We are the peo - ple

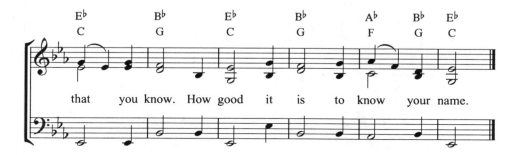

that you know. How good it is to know your name.

2. How good it is to sing to you.
   You are the God who heals our wrong.
   You are the home where we belong.
   How good it is to sing to you.

3. How good it is to find you near.
   We are the seed – you make us grow.
   You are the leaven, we the dough.
   How good it is to find you near.

4. How good it is to sing to you.
   You are the bread that makes us strong.
   You are the reason for our song.
   How good it is to sing to you.

82 I am tired and I a stranger

Attributed to St Columba (6th century)

Angela Reith
arr. Keith Duke

83 I bind unto myself today

From *St Patrick's Breastplate*
trans. Cecil Frances Alexander

Traditional Irish melodies
arr. Keith Duke

ST PATRICK DLM

1. I bind un - to my - self to - day the
2. I bind this day to me for e - ver, by
3. I bind un - to my - self to - day the
4. I bind un - to my - self to - day the
6. I bind un - to my - self the name, the

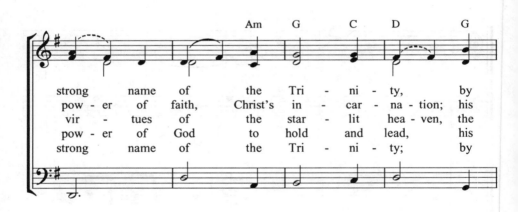

strong name of the Tri - ni - ty, by
pow - er of faith, Christ's in - car - na - tion; his
vir - tues of the star - lit hea - ven, the
pow - er of God to hold and lead, his
strong name of the Tri - ni - ty; by

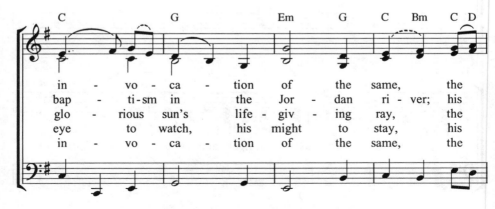

in - vo - ca - tion of the same, the
bap - ti - sm in the Jor - dan ri - ver; his
glo - rious sun's life - giv - ing ray, the
eye to watch, his might to stay, his
in - vo - ca - tion of the same, the

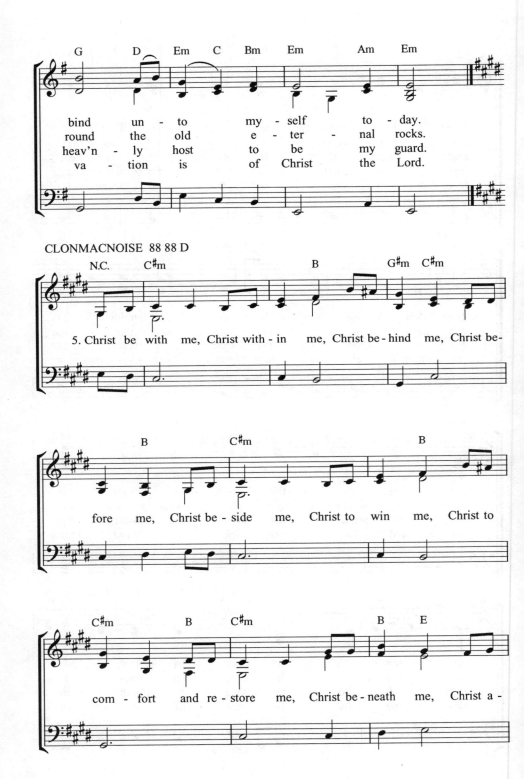

bind un - to my - self to - day.
round the old e - ter - nal rocks.
heav'n - ly host to be my guard.
va - tion is of Christ the Lord.

CLONMACNOISE 88 88 D

5. Christ be with me, Christ with - in me, Christ be - hind me, Christ be-

fore me, Christ be - side me, Christ to win me, Christ to

com - fort and re - store me, Christ be - neath me, Christ a -

bove me, Christ in qui - et, Christ in dan - ger, Christ in

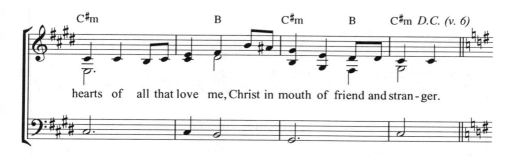

hearts of all that love me, Christ in mouth of friend and stran - ger.

84 I dream of a church

Kate Compston

Keith Duke

1. I dream of a church that joins in with God's laugh-ing as she rocks in her rap-ture, en-joy-ing her art: she's glad of her world, in its risk - ing and grow-ing, 'tis the child she has

borne   and holds close   to her heart.

2. I dream of a church that joins in with God's weeping
as she crouches, weighed down by the sorrow she sees:
she cries for the hostile, the cold and no-hoping,
for she bears in herself our despair and dis-ease.

3. I dream of a church that joins in with God's dancing
as she moves like the wind and the wave and the fire:
a church that can pick up its skirts, pirouetting,
with the steps that can signal God's deepest desire.

4. I dream of a church that joins in with God's loving
as she bends to embrace the unlovely and lost,
a church that can free, by its sharing and daring,
the imprisoned and poor, and then shoulder the cost.

5. God, make us a church that joins in with your living,
as you cherish and challenge, rein in and release,
a church that is winsome, impassioned, inspiring;
lioness of your justice and lamb of your peace.

85 I give myself to you, Lord

David Adam

Dedications

Keith Duke

1. I give my-self to you, Lord, I give my-self to

you; with my mind and its think - ing I give my-self to

you. My life cries out for you, Lord, my life cries out for

you. I give my life to you, Lord, I give my life to

2. I give my heart to you, Lord, I give my heart to you;
   with my soul and its loving, I give my heart to you;
   my love cries out for you, Lord, my love cries out for you;
   I give my love to you, Lord, I give my love to you;
   I give my love to you.

3. I give my hands to you, Lord, I give my hands to you;
   with my body and its action, I give my hands to you;
   my strength cries out for you, Lord, my strength cries out for you;
   I give my work to you, Lord, I give my work to you;
   I give my work to you.

4. I give my plans to you, Lord, I give my plans to you;
   with my heart and its yearnings, I give my plans to you;
   my will cries out for you, Lord, my will cries out for you;
   I give my hopes to you, Lord, I give my hopes to you;
   I give my hopes to you.

5. I give my life to you, Lord, I give my life to you;
   please keep me true to you, Lord, I give my life to you;
   my soul cries out for you, Lord, my soul cries out for you;
   I give myself to you, Lord, I give myself to you;
   I give myself to you.

86 In a byre near Bethlehem

Iona Community

Traditional Irish melody
arr. Keith Duke

WILD MOUNTAIN THYME 78 78 6 and Refrain

1. In a byre near Beth-le-hem, passed by ma - ny a wand-'ring stran-ger, the most pre - cious Word of Life was heard gurg - ling in a man-ger for the good of us all. And he's here when we call him bring-ing

health, love and laugh-ter to life now and e - ver af - ter, for the good of us all.

2. By the Galilean Lake
   where the people flocked for teaching,
   the most precious Word of Life
   fed their mouths as well as preaching,
   for the good of us all.

3. Quiet was Gethsemane,
   camouflaging priest and soldier;
   the most precious Word of Life
   took the world's weight on his shoulder,
   for the good of us all.

87 In Christ alone

Stuart Townend and Keith Getty

Stuart Townend and Keith Getty
arr. Keith Duke

1. In Christ a - lone my hope is found, he is my

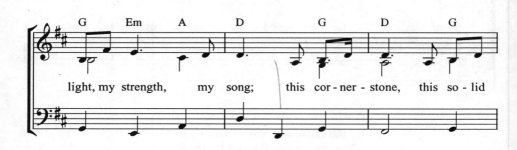

light, my strength, my song; this cor - ner - stone, this so - lid

ground, firm through the fierc-est drought and storm. What heights of

love, what depths of peace, when fears are stilled, when striv-ings

cease! My com - for - ter, my all in

all, here in the love of Christ I stand.

2. In Christ alone! – who took on flesh,
   fulness of God in helpless babe!
   This gift of love and righteousness,
   scorned by the ones he came to save:
   till on that cross as Jesus died,
   the wrath of God was satisfied –
   for ev'ry sin on him was laid;
   here in the death of Christ I live.

3. There in the ground his body lay,
   light of the world by darkness slain:
   then bursting forth in glorious day
   up from the grave he rose again!
   And as he stands in victory
   sin's curse has lost its grip on me,
   for I am his and he is mine –
   bought with the precious blood of Christ.

4. No guilt in life, no fear in death,
   this is the pow'r of Christ in me;
   from life's first cry to final breath,
   Jesus commands my destiny.
   No pow'r of hell, no scheme of man,
   can ever pluck me from his hand;
   till he returns or calls me home,
   here in the pow'r of Christ I'll stand!

CELTIC
HYMN BOOK

88 In her house there is a table   *Wisdom's table*

Doug Gay

Doug Gay
arr. Keith Duke

WISDOM'S TABLE 87 87 and Refrain

1. In her house there is a table, rich-ly laid with bread and wine.
All the fool-ish are in-vi-ted, she calls to us, 'Come, and dine.'

Refrain
Come and eat at Wis-dom's ta-ble, come and lay your bur-den down;
come and learn the pow'r of weak-ness, Wis-dom's cross and Wis-dom's crown.

2. In this world we will have trouble
and our comforters will fail;
all our answers will seem useless,
all our hopes will seem unreal.

3. There are roads which lead to danger,
there are paths which lead to life:
Wisdom's ways are filled with choices
for the trav'llers she invites.

4. There are those who search for reasons,
there are those who look for signs:
Wisdom dances on the tombstone
of the fool who bled and died.

89 In my Father's house

Paul Kyle

Paul Kyle
arr. Keith Duke

In my Fa-ther's house there are ma - ny man - sions.

In my Fa-ther's house there is one for me.

In my Fa-ther's house I will live for e - ver.

There and there a - lone shall my dwel - ling be.

What more could we ask than this ho - ly plea-sure?

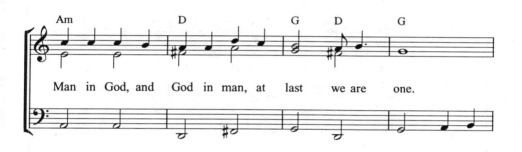

Man in God, and God in man, at last we are one.

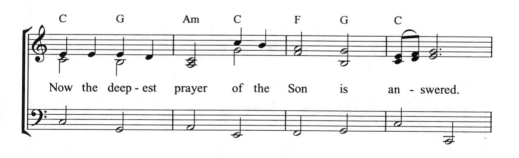

Now the deep - est prayer of the Son is an - swered.

And sal - va - tion's work is com - plete - ly done.

90 In our journeying this day

Traveller's prayer

David Adam

Keith Duke

In our jour-ney-ing this day, keep us, Fa-ther, in your way. In seek-ing of a vis-ion true, keep us, Sa-viour, close to you. In our de-sire to do your will, keep us, Spi-rit, guide us still. In our striv-ing to be free, keep and help us, blest Tri-ni-ty.

91 In the morning I will sing

From the Liturgy

Traditional arr. Keith Duke
Psalm tone: Keith Duke

In the morn-ing I will sing glad songs of praise to you.

1. O God, you are my God, and I long for you from
   early morning; my whole being desires you
   like a dry, worn-out and waterless land,
   my soul is thirsty for you.

2. Let me see you in the house of prayer, let me
   see how mighty and glorious you are;
   your constant love is better than life itself,
   and so I will praise you.

3. I will give thanks as long as I live; I will
   raise my hands to you in prayer.
   My soul will feast and be satisfied, and I will
   sing glad songs of praise to you.

4. In the shadow of your wings I sing for joy.
   I cling to you and your hand keeps me safe.

5. Glory to the Father, and to the Son, and to
   the Holy Spirit; as it was in the beginning,
   is now, and shall be for ever.

92 In the place of fear

Ray Simpson   Jacynth Hamill

1. In the place of fear; God's strength to up-hold me.

2. In the place of emp-ti-ness; God's wis-dom there to guide me.

3. In the place of con-fu-sion; God's eye for my see-ing.

4. In the place of dis-cord; God's ear for my hear-ing.

CELTIC
HYMN BOOK

93 In the place of stillness

Christ in quiet

David Adam

Keith Duke

In the place of still-ness: the room of prayer,
in the sanc-tua-ry of a-dor-a-tion.
In the stil-ling of the storm, in the stil-ling of our
minds, our souls and bo-dies; in the
peace he gives, in the peace he asks us to share.

94 In the power of the Creator

David Adam

Keith Duke

($\bullet$ = 76)

Unison

In the po-wer of the Cre - a- tor, in the peace of the Re-deem-er, in the pre-sence of the Spi - rit we wel - come you. Three in your com-ing, Three with you

95 In the silence of the stars

Speak, Lord

David Adam

Rosemary Turnbull
arr. Keith Duke

2. In the stillness of this room,
   in the calming of my mind,
   in the longing of my heart,
   speak, Lord.

3. In the voice of a friend,
   in the chatter of a child,
   in the words of a stranger,
   speak, Lord.

4. In the op'ning of a book,
   in the looking at a film,
   in the listening to music,
   speak, Lord, for your servant listens.

96 Into the Sacred Three I immerse you

Ray Simpson

Keith Duke

In-to the Sac - red Three I im-merse you, in-to their pow'r and peace I place you; may their breath be yours to live, may their love be yours to give. In-to the Sac - red Three I im-merse you.

CELTIC
HYMN BOOK

97 I place my hands in yours

David Adam

Angela Reith
arr. Keith Duke

I place my hands in yours, Lord,

I put my hands in yours.

2. I place my will in yours, Lord,
   I place my will in yours.

3. I place my thoughts in yours, Lord,
   I place my thoughts in yours.

4. I place my heart in yours, Lord,
   I place my heart in yours.

5. I place my days in yours, Lord,
   I place my days in yours.

6. I place my life in yours, Lord,
   I place my life in yours.

98 I, the Lord of sea and sky

Here I am, Lord

Dan Schutte
based on Isaiah 6

Dan Schutte
arr. Keith Duke

HERE I AM 77 74 D and Refrain

1. I, the Lord of sea and sky, I have heard my peo-ple cry. All who dwell in dark and sin my hand will save. I, who made the stars of night, I will make their dark-ness bright. Who will bear my light to them? Whom shall I send?

Here I

2. I, the Lord of snow and rain,
   I have borne my people's pain.
   I have wept for love of them.
   They turn away.
   I will break their hearts of stone,
   give them hearts for love alone.
   I will speak my word to them.
   Whom shall I send?

3. I, the Lord of wind and flame,
   I will tend the poor and lame.
   I will set a feast for them.
   My hand will save.
   Finest bread I will provide
   till their hearts be satisfied.
   I will give my life to them.
   Whom shall I send?

99 I will pray that God

Sammy Horner

Sammy Horner
arr. Keith Duke

I will pray that God will touch your life, I will pray that all will bless you. I will pray that hope will fill your mind, and that faith will stand a-round you. May grace and trust fre-quent your house, and

100 Jesus, be the centre

Be the centre

Michael Frye

Michael Frye
arr. Keith Duke

Je - sus, be the cen - tre, be my

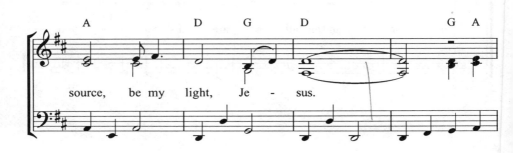

source, be my light, Je - sus.

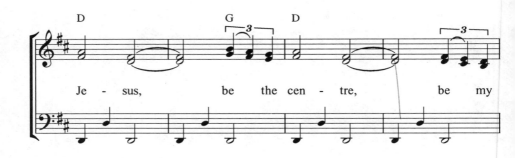

Je - sus, be the cen - tre, be my

hope, be my song, Je - sus. Be the

fire in my heart, be the wind in these sails, be the

rea-son that I live, Je - sus, Je - sus.

Je - sus, be my vi - sion, be my

path, be my guide, Je - sus.

101 Jesus calls us here to meet him

John L. Bell
Graham Maule

Traditional Scottish melody from Lewis
arr. Keith Duke

1. Jesus calls us here to meet him as, through word and song and prayer, we affirm God's promised presence where his people live and care. Praise the God who keeps his promise;

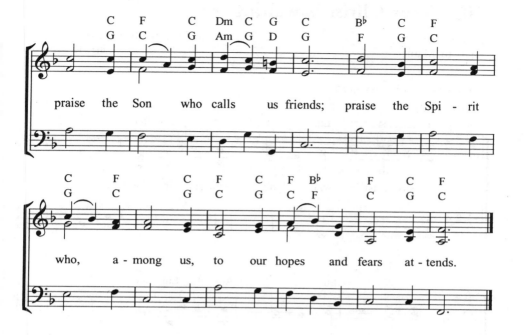

praise the Son who calls us friends; praise the Spi - rit who, a - mong us, to our hopes and fears at - tends.

2. Jesus calls us to confess him
   Word of Life and Lord of all,
   sharer of our flesh and frailness
   saving all who fail or fall.
   Tell his holy human story;
   tell his tales that all may hear;
   tell the world that Christ in glory
   came to earth to meet us here.

3. Jesus calls us to each other:
   vastly diff'rent though we are;
   race and colour, class and gender
   neither limit nor debar.
   Join the hand of friend and stranger;
   join the hands of age and youth;
   join the faithful and the doubter
   in their common search for truth.

4. Jesus calls us to his table
   rooted firm in time and space,
   where the church in earth and heaven
   finds a common meeting-place.
   Share the bread and wine, his body;
   share the love of which we sing;
   share the feast for saints and sinners
   hosted by our Lord and King.

102 Jesus Christ is waiting

John L. Bell
Graham Maule

Traditional French melody
arr. Keith Duke

NOËL NOUVELET 65 65 55 65

($\rlap{/}{\text{o}}$ = 80)

1. Je - sus Christ is wait - ing, wait-ing in the streets.

No one is his neigh - bour, all a - lone he eats.

Lis - ten, Lord Je - sus, I am lone - ly too.

Make me, friend or stran - ger, fit to wait on you.

2. Jesus Christ is raging,
   raging in the streets,
   where injustice spirals
   and real hope retreats.
   Listen, Lord Jesus,
   I am angry too;
   in the Kingdom's causes
   let me rage with you.

3. Jesus Christ is healing,
   healing in the streets
   curing those who suffer,
   touching those he greets.
   Listen, Lord Jesus,
   I have pity too;
   let my care be active,
   healing just like you.

4. Jesus Christ is dancing,
   dancing in the streets,
   where each sign of hatred
   he, with love, defeats.
   Listen, Lord Jesus,
   I should triumph too;
   where good conquers evil,
   let me dance with you.

5. Jesus Christ is calling,
   calling in the streets,
   'Who will join my journey?
   I will guide your feet.'
   Listen, Lord Jesus,
   let my fears be few;
   walk one step before me,
   I will follow you.

CELTIC
HYMN BOOK

103 Jesus Christ, Son of God

Traditional Liturgy

John L. Bell

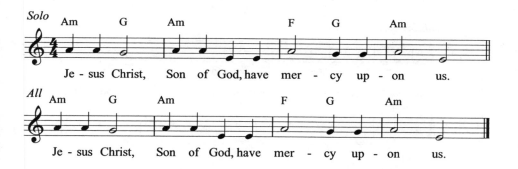

104 Jesus, draw me ever nearer
May this journey

Margaret Becker

Keith Getty
arr. Keith Duke

With feeling (♩ = 72)

1. Je - sus, draw me e - ver near - er as I la - bour through the storm. You have called me to this pas - sage, and I'll fol - low though I'm worn. May this jour - ney bring a bles - sing, may I rise on wings of faith; and at the

end of   my heart's test-ing,   with your like-ness   let me   wake.

2. Jesus, guide me through the tempest,
   keep my spirit staid and sure.
   When the midnight meets the morning,
   let me love you even more.

3. Let the treasures of the trial
   form within me as I go.
   And at the end of this long passage,
   let me leave them at your throne.

105 Jesus, Lamb of God

Adapted from the Liturgy
by Ray Simpson

J. Mease
arr. Keith Duke

GARTAN 88 88

(♩ = 92)

Je - sus, Lamb of God, have mer - cy; bear - er of our
sins, have mer - cy; Sa - viour of the world, Lord Je - sus,
may your peace be with us al - ways.

106 Kindle a flame

John L. Bell
Graham Maule

John L. Bell
Graham Maule

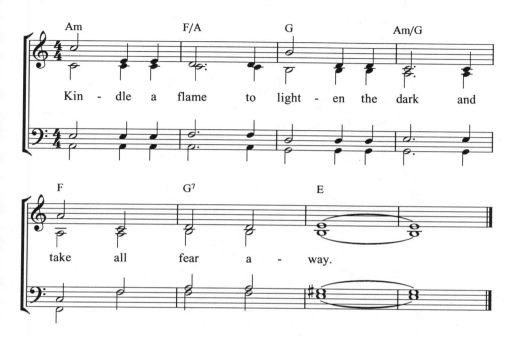

Kin - dle a flame to light - en the dark and take all fear a - way.

CELTIC
HYMN BOOK

107 Kindle in my heart today

Ray Simpson

Ray Simpson
arr. Keith Duke

1. Kin - dle in my heart to-day warmth of
2. Kin - dle in my work to-day
3. Kin - dle in my world to-day

friend - ship, fire of love. Burn a - way the dross, the

fey, shine with - in, a - round, a - bove.

108 Lamb of God

From the Liturgy

James MacMillan
from the *Galloway Mass*

Lamb of God, you take a - way the sins of the world, have mer - cy on us. Lamb of God, you take a - way the sins of the world, have mer - cy on us.

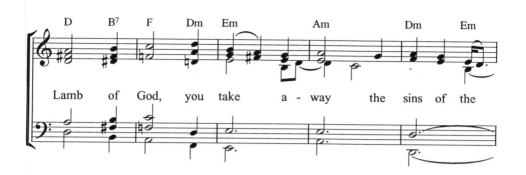

Lamb of God, you take a - way the sins of the

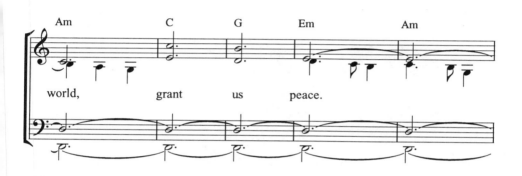

world, grant us peace.

Keyboard

CELTIC
HYMN BOOK

109 Lead me from death to life

Peace prayer

Adapted from *The Upanishads*
by Satish Kumar

Donald Swann

Lead me from death to life, from false-hood to truth. Lead me from des-pair to hope, from fear to trust. Lead me from hate to love, from war to peace, let peace fill our heart, our world, our u-ni-verse.

110 Let glory and blessing flow down

Graham Booth

Graham Booth
arr. Keith Duke

Let glo - ry and bles - sing flow down from your throne;
life - giv - ing wa - ter, and blood to a - tone. Your
cross raised on high in ex - tra - va - gant love, your
mer - cy un - bound - ed and poured from a - bove.

Refrain
Grace, grace, more of your grace;

2. So drink from the water, delight in his care.
   Deeper and deeper, he's much more to share.
   Now let him come to you, look full in his face;
   just rest in his arms, feel his loving embrace.

3. He wants so to fill us that others may see
   his love and mercy spill over – so free.
   Holy Spirit, empow'r us with love for the lost;
   his passion, his justice – for he paid the cost.

4. We long, loving Father, that glory flow out;
   fire of your presence in grace spread about.
   We long that your grace and your glory become
   the harvest of lives giving praise to your Son.

111 Let there be peace on earth

Let it begin with me

Sy Miller and Jill Jackson
(♩. = 60)

Sy Miller and Jill Jackson
arr. Keith Duke

Let there be peace on earth, and let it be-gin with me; let there be peace on earth, the peace that was meant to be. With God as our Fa-ther, bro-thers / sis-ters all are we. Let me walk with my bro-ther / sis-ter in per-fect har-mo-ny. Let peace be-gin with

112 Let us be candles

Toby D. Griffen

Toby D. Griffen
arr. Keith Duke

1. Let us be can - dles on a stand and show all the earth the way of thy saints: Du - bri - cius' light that doth com - mand the dark - ness shrink back and loose its con - straints.

2. Faith - ful as Bren - dan let us sail on o - ceans un -

known, through tem - pest and shock, hold - ing thy way through

all tra - vail with Non - na's ten - a - cious grasp on the rock.

3. Sitting in quiet Ita's cell,
   we listen for thee to give thy command,
   even though sacrifice may well
   with Cadoc present us into thy hand.

4. Give us an ounce of Ciaran's grace,
   so we might treat others amiably
   and create friendships through the race
   of humans, as Maedoc* showeth for thee.

5. Show us to care as Brigid did
   in love for the hungry, poor, and afraid,
   healing the sick who to us bid,
   as they did to Beuno* for loving aid.

6. Lead us to learn about thy Word,
   as Hildutus did, the better to know
   on what great mission for our Lord
   with Samson beside us we ought to go.

7. Ninian's bravery we ask
   to carry us through the trials we face,
   looking to Ia in our task –
   persistence we need to finish the race.

8. Let us in all humility
   each other serve as Monenna hath shown,
   as in Iona's harmony
   they did when Columba's hearth
      warmly shown.

9. Bring us, O Lord, to tell thy deed,
   inspired by David's eloquent speech,
   also with Samthann do we plead;
   true spirituality let us reach.

10. Show us forgiveness that we may
    from Patrick's example all learn to live
    firmly united in thy way,
    as thou in thy Cross example dost give.

11. So let us praise the Lord above
    with all of the saints who dwelling below
    show us in dedicated love
    how we may be saints with spirits aglow.

* Maedoc – pronounced 'Meedoc'
* Beuno – pronounced 'Byeno'

113 Lighten our darkness

David Adam

Keith Duke

1. Light - en our dark - ness, Lord, we pray.
Light - en our dark - ness at the end of the day. De - fend us from dan - ger and per - ils of the night, for the love of Je - sus the Lord who is light.

2. Lighten our burden, Lord, we ask.
   Lighten our burden, bring joy to the task;
   give peace in our labours,
   to work bring your might,
   for the love of Jesus the Lord who is light.

114 Lighten our darkness

David Adam

John Scarfe
arr. Keith Duke

1. Light - en our dark - ness, Lord, we pray.
Light - en our dark - ness at the end of the day. De -
fend us from dan - ger and per - ils this night, for the
love of Je - sus, the Lord who is light.

2. Lighten our burden, Lord, we ask.
Lighten our burden, bring joy to the task.
Give peace in our labours,
to work bring your might,
for the love of Jesus the Lord who is light.

115 Light of the world

Paul Gibson

Keith Duke

Now as we see the lights of eve-ning

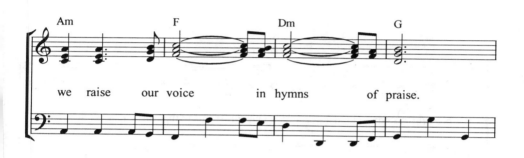

we raise our voice in hymns of praise.

Wor - thy are you of end - less bles-sing,

sun of our night, lamp of our days.

116 Long years ago

Traditional Cornish

Geoff Nobes

1. Long years a-go, a-cross the wes-tern wa - ter winds
brought to this our shore. One glo-rious with - in, a king's own
daugh-ter, to teach our land Christ's law. The saints of
God his glo-ry are: can-ta-te Do-mi-no, al-le-lu -

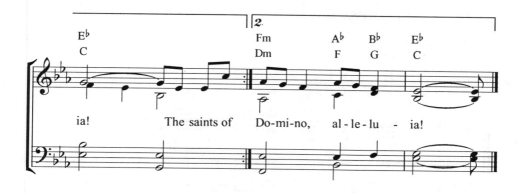

2. Throughout her days God's little flock she tended,
   a faithful shepherd she,
   leading the sheep her patient love defended
   against the wilderness.

117 Lord, bless us

Colin Hodgetts
based on St Columba

Song of Saint Columba

Colin Hodgetts

1. Lord, bless us that we bless you, cre - a - tor and con - ser - vor of heav'n and all its or - ders of land and strand and wa - ters;

2. that we may search the writings
that give the soul renewal;
that we may read around us
such beauty as will feed us;

3. that we may find within us
the letters of your loving;
that we may have such living
as any soul will freshen.

4. At times we kneel to heaven,
at times the psalms are singing,
at times are contemplating
our King, our holy leader.

5. At times we are delighting
in work that lacks compulsion;
at times we gather seaweed,
at times we go out fishing,

6. at times we seed and harvest;
at times we feed your creatures,
and feed the poor, our brothers;
at times we sit in silence.

118 Lord, by your death   *Memorial Acclamation*

Michael Forster

Traditional Gaelic melody
arr. Keith Duke

BUNESSAN 55 54 D

Lord, by your death and, Lord, by your ris - ing, you have re-deemed us, set - ting us free. You are the Sa - viour of all cre - a - tion. Come now in glo - ry, that all may see.

119 Lord, from this world's stormy sea

David Adam

Traditional Irish melody
adapted by Jacynth Hamill
arr. Keith Duke

lift me up and keep me sane; Lord, lift me

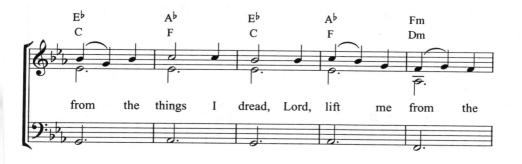

from the things I dread, Lord, lift me from the

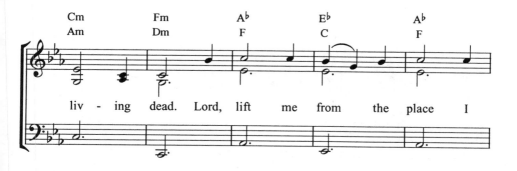

liv - ing dead. Lord, lift me from the place I

lie; Lord, lift me that I ne - ver die.

120 Lord, I cry to you

Graham Booth

Graham Booth

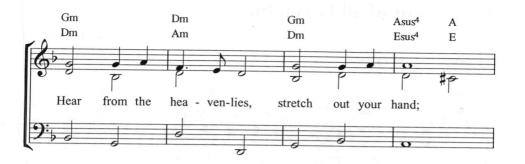

Hear from the hea - ven-lies, stretch out your hand;

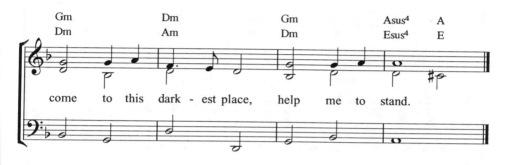

come to this dark - est place, help me to stand.

2. Lord, I cry to you, hear my prayer,
   Lord, I cry to you, heal my despair.
   Covenant God of love, I feel so alone;
   Jesus, where are you now with blood to atone?
   Hear from Gethsemane, stretch out your hand
   into this desp'rate place, help me to stand.

3. Lord, I cry to you, hear my prayer,
   Lord, I cry to you, heal my despair.
   Calm my anxieties, take, Lord, my pain;
   bathe me with holy love again and again.
   Hear from your cross of love, stretch out your hand;
   dwell in this inner place, help me to stand.

121 Lord of all hopefulness

Jan Struther

Traditional Irish melody
arr. Keith Duke

SLANE 10 11 11 12

1. Lord of all hope-ful-ness, Lord of all joy, whose trust, e - ver child-like, no cares could des - troy, be there at our wak-ing, and give us, we pray, your bliss in our hearts, Lord, at the break of the day.

Last time

2. Lord of all eagerness,
   Lord of all faith,
   whose strong hands were skilled
   at the plane and the lathe,
   be there at our labours,
   and give us, we pray,
   your strength in our hearts, Lord,
   at the noon of the day.

3. Lord of all kindliness,
   Lord of all grace,
   your hands swift to welcome,
   your arms to embrace,
   be there at our homing,
   and give us, we pray,
   your love in our hearts, Lord,
   at the eve of the day.

4. Lord of all gentleness,
   Lord of all calm,
   whose voice is contentment,
   whose presence is balm,
   be there at our sleeping,
   and give us, we pray,
   your peace in our hearts, Lord,
   at the end of the day.

122 Lord of life, we come to you

Catherine Walker

Traditional Gaelic melody
arr. Keith Duke

ERISKAY LOVE LILT 77 66

Lord of life, we come to you, Lord of all, our Sa-viour be; come to bless and to heal with the light of your life.

From the Liturgy

Traditional Gaelic melody
arr. Keith Duke

ERISKAY LOVE LILT 77 67

Ky-ri - e e - le - i - son. Ky-ri - e e - le - i- son. Lord, have mer - cy on us. Ky-ri - e e - le - i - son.

123 Lord, strengthen every good

The conqueror

David Adam

Jacques Berthier

2. Lord, strengthen ev'ry light,
   defeat the pow'r of darkness;
   Lord, strengthen ev'ry light,
   defeat the pow'r of darkness.

CELTIC
HYMN BOOK

124 Lord, to whom shall we go?

From John 6:68

John L. Bell

Lord, to whom shall we go? Yours are the words of e - ter - nal life.

125 Lord, we come to ask your healing

Jean Holloway

Keith Duke

1. Lord, we come to ask your heal-ing, teach us of love; all un-spok-en shame re-veal-ing, teach us of love. Take our self-ish thoughts and ac-tions, pet-ty feuds, de-vi-sive fac-tions, hear us now to

May also be sung to *Ar hyd y nos* (No. 193)

2. Soothe away our pain and sorrow,
   hold us in love;
   grace we cannot buy or borrow,
   hold us in love.
   Though we see but dark and danger,
   though we spurn both friend and stranger,
   though we often dread tomorrow,
   hold us in love.

3. When the bread is raised and broken,
   fill us with love;
   words of consecration spoken,
   fill us with love.
   As our grateful prayers continue,
   make the faith that we have in you
   more than just an empty token,
   fill us with love.

4. Help us live for one another,
   bind us in love;
   stranger, neighbour, father, mother –
   bind us in love.
   All are equal at your table,
   through your Spirit make us able
   to embrace as sister, brother,
   bind us in love.

126 Lord, we have heard

Paul Kyle

Paul Kyle
arr. Keith Duke

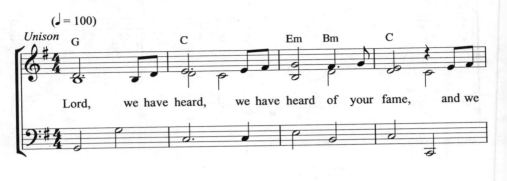

Lord, we have heard, we have heard of your fame, and we

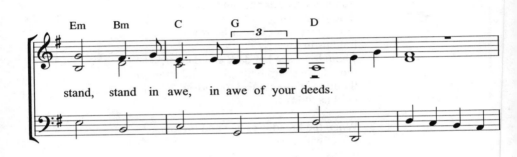

stand, stand in awe, in awe of your deeds.

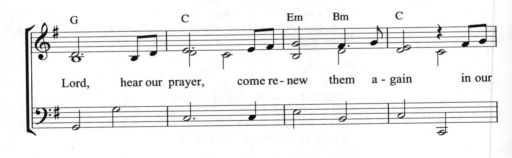

Lord, hear our prayer, come re-new them a-gain in our

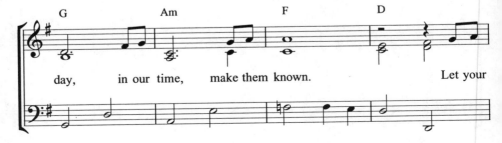

day, in our time, make them known. Let your

glo - ry, let your glo - ry, let your

glo - ry fill the earth. Fa-ther,

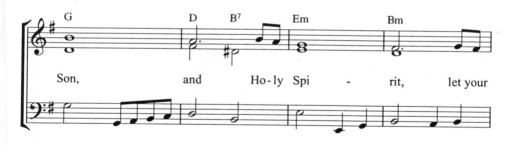

Son, and Ho-ly Spi - rit, let your

glo - ry fill the earth.

127 Lord, you are my island

Based on a prayer of
St Columba

Nicholas Hopton

1. Lord, you are my is-land, in your shield-ing grace I

build my nest. Lord, you are the calm sea in whose

per-fect peace I find true rest. You're the san-dy shore,

you're the brea-kers' roar, you're my

is-land, Lord: my sal - va - tion.

2. Lord, you are my island,
   you're a harbour sheltered, a mooring safe.
   Lord, you are my cliff,
   taking all the force of the pounding waves.
   You're the seabirds' yell, you're the leaping swell,
   you're my island, Lord: my salvation.

3. Lord, you are my island,
   you're the otter's track on the clinging wrack.
   Lord, you are my island,
   you're a zephyr breeze bidding me take ease.
   You're the selkie's song, you're an anchor strong,
   you're my island, Lord: my salvation.

4. Lord, you are my island,
   in your shielding grace I build my nest.
   Lord, you are the calm sea,
   in whose perfect peace I find true rest.
   You're the sandy shore, you're the breakers' roar,
   you're my island, Lord: my salvation.

128 Love is patient

Keith Duke
based on 1 Corinthians 13:1-7

Keith Duke

This may be sung as a round with entries as indicated.

2. Never jealous, never sour,
   quietly helping, never loud;
   never selfish, conceited or proud;
   Lord, give us love.

Repeat verse 1

129 Magnificat

Ray Simpson

Traditional American melody
arr. Keith Duke

130 Maker maternal

Michael Forster

Kevin Mayhew
arr. Keith Duke

1. Ma - ker ma - ter - nal, mak - ing and mend - ing,
tak - ing and tend - ing all whom you bear;
glad - ly you love us, sad - ly re - prove us,
no - thing can move us out of your care.

2. Love full of beauty,
showing and sharing,
cradling and caring
in your embrace,
each of us knowing,
tenderness showing,
watching us growing,
giving us space.

3. Mother eternal,
touching and tending,
seeking and sending,
fill us with grace;
stir and amaze us,
chide us and praise us,
lovingly raise us
up to your face.

131 May our prayers rise like incense

Traditional Liturgy

Traditional
arr. Keith Duke

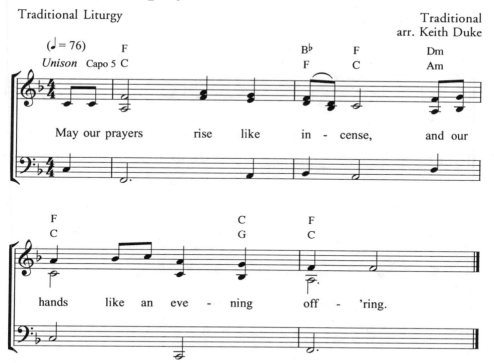

May our prayers rise like in - cense, and our

hands like an eve - ning off - 'ring.

132 May the eternal glory shine upon you

Ray Simpson

Keith Duke

133 May the peace of the Lord Christ go with you

P. Sutcliffe

P. Sutcliffe

134 May your life in this world

The blessing

Sammy Horner

Sammy Horner
arr. Keith Duke

May your life in this world be a hap-py one, may the

sun be warm and may the skies be blue. May each

storm that comes your way clear the air for a bright-er day, may the

saints and Sa-viour watch o - ver you.

1. As you
2. As you

make your way through this old world of ours, as you
spend your time with your friends and your fa - mi - ly, as you

(verse 2)

see the beau - ty of the morn - ing dew, as you
see the warmth and love they have for you, as you

smell the sum - mer flow-ers, as you pass a-way the hours, may the
see the wars and hate that o-thers ra - di - ate, may the

To continue | Last time

Refrain

saints and Sa-viour watch o - ver you. May your
saints and Sa-viour watch o - ver you.

135 Morning has broken

Eleanor Farjeon

Traditional Gaelic melody
arr. Keith Duke

2. Sweet the rain's new fall,
   sunlit from heaven,
   like the first dew-fall
   on the first grass.
   Praise for the sweetness
   of the wet garden,
   sprung in completeness
   where his feet pass.

3. Mine is the sunlight!
   Mine is the morning
   born of the one light
   Eden saw play!
   Praise with elation,
   praise ev'ry morning,
   God's re-creation
   of the new day!

136 Mothering God

Jean Janzen
based on Julian of Norwich

Janet Peachey
arr. Keith Duke

1. Mo-ther-ing God, you gave me birth in the bright morn-ing of this world. Cre-a-tor, source of ev-'ry breath, you are my rain, my wind, my sun; you are my rain, my wind, my sun.

2. Mothering Christ, you took my form,
offering me your food of light,
grain of life, and grape of love,
your very body for my peace;
your very body for my peace.

3. Mothering Spirit, nurturing one,
in arms of patience hold me close,
so that in faith I root and grow
until I flower, until I know;
until I flower, until I know.

CELTIC
HYMN BOOK

137 My life is in your hands

Ray Simpson

Ray Simpson
arr. Keith Duke

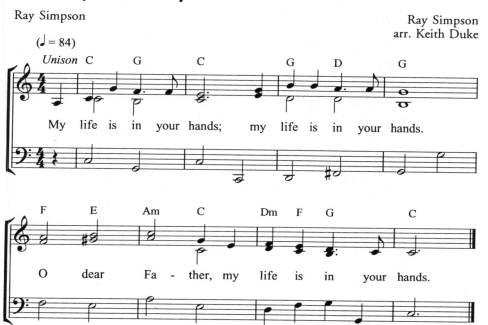

My life is in your hands; my life is in your hands.

O dear Fa - ther, my life is in your hands.

138 My soul is filled with joy

Magnificat

Unknown, based on Luke 1:46-55

Scottish folk melody
arr. Keith Duke

WILD MOUNTAIN THYME

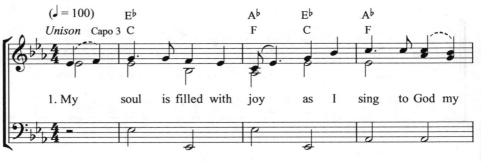

1. My soul is filled with joy as I sing to God my

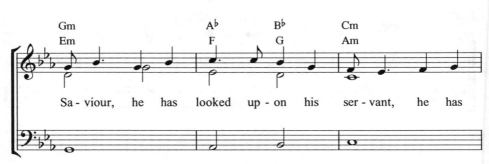

Sa - viour, he has looked up - on his ser - vant, he has

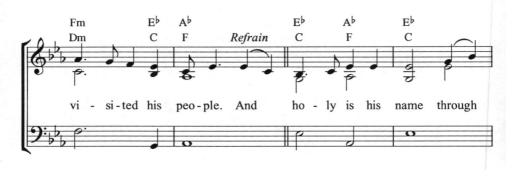

vi - si - ted his peo - ple. And *Refrain* ho - ly is his name through

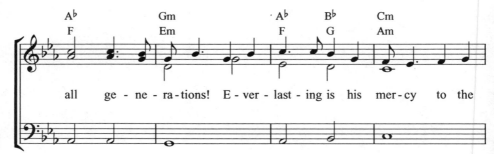

all ge - ne - ra - tions! E - ver - last - ing is his mer - cy to the

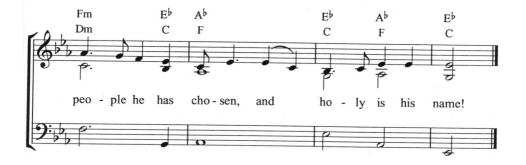

peo - ple he has cho - sen, and ho - ly is his name!

2. I am lowly as a child,
   but I know from this day forward
   that my name will be remembered
   and the world will call me blessèd.

3. I proclaim the pow'r of God!
   He does marvels for his servants;
   though he scatters the proud-hearted
   and destroys the might of princes.

4. To the hungry he gives food,
   sends the rich away empty.
   In his mercy he is mindful
   of the people he has chosen.

5. In his love he now fulfils
   what he promised to our fathers.
   I will praise the Lord, my Saviour.
   Everlasting is his mercy.

139 North, East, South and West

Place blessing

Andy Baggott

Keith Duke

(♩ = 92)

Unison

North, East, South and West, I ask this cir - cle to be blessed. Earth be - low me, sky a - bove, Cre - a - tor, fill this place with love.

140 Now go in the peace of Christ

Traditional

Unknown
arr. Keith Duke

Now go in the peace of Christ. Thanks be to God.

141 Now listen, all you people

Margaret Harvey
based on Psalm 78:1-7

Traditional Welsh melody
arr. Keith Duke

YN Y MOR 76 73 77 76 10

deeds, we'll tell this ge - ne - ra - tion of God's deeds.

2. He gave his law to Israel
   in his love, his commands,
   how wonderful, to Jacob
   his commands.
   Our forebears were instructed
   to teach each generation
   and children tell their children
   to remember God's law,
   always to trust God and obey his law.

142 O for a thousand tongues to sing

Charles Wesley

Traditional Irish melody
arr. Keith Duke

STAR OF THE COUNTY DOWN

(♩ = 92)

Unison

1. O for a thou - sand tongues to sing my

great Re - deem - er's praise, the glo - ries of my

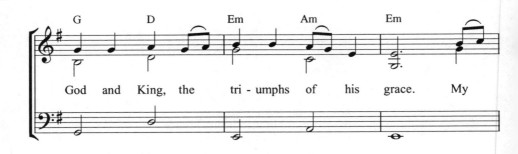

God and King, the tri - umphs of his grace. My

gra - cious mas - ter and my God, as - sist me to pro -

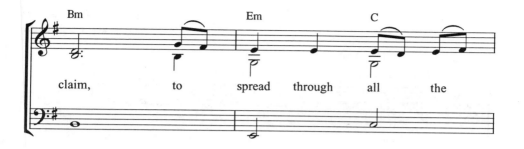

claim, to spread through all the

earth a - broad the ho - nours of your name.

2. Jesus! The name that charms our fears,
   that bids our sorrows cease;
   'tis music in the sinners ears,
   'tis life and health and peace.
   He breaks the pow'r of cancelled sin,
   he sets the pris'ners free;
   his blood can make the foulest clean;
   his blood availed for me.

3. He speaks, and list'ning to his voice
   new life the dead receive,
   the mournful broken hearts rejoice,
   the humble poor believe.
   Hear him, you deaf; his praise, you dumb
   your loosened tongues employ;
   you blind, behold your Saviour come;
   and leap you lame for joy.

143 O God of the elements

Carmina Gadelica

Celtic aire *Ag Chriost an Sìol*
arr. Keith Duke

O God of the e - le - ments, O

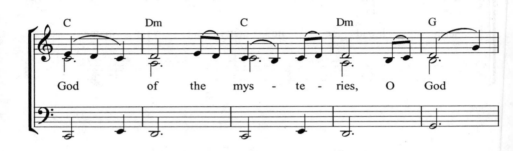

God of the mys - te - ries, O God

of the foun - tains, O King of kings, O

King of kings! Thy joy the joy, thy light the

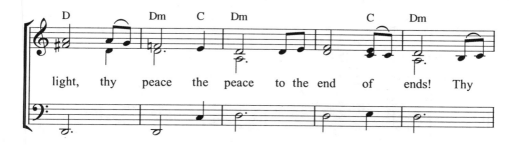

light, thy peace the peace to the end of ends! Thy

joy the joy, thy light the light, thy peace the

peace to the end of ends!

144 O happy are those

Margaret Harvey
based on Psalm 1

Traditional Welsh melody
arr. Keith Duke

THE ASH GROVE 12 11 12 11 D

2. But like winnowed chaff blown away by the strong wind
   the godless, when judged, are not able to stand.
   They will not find room among those who are just, but
   like dry straw are blown from the face of the land.
   But all who love God are protected and guided,
   for God's way is life, and apart from him, none.
   O happy are those who reject evil counsel,
   their joy in the blessings that come from his hand.

145 Oh, the life of the world

Kathy Galloway

I. Galloway
arr. Keith Duke

LIFE OF THE WORLD Irregular
(♩ = 104)

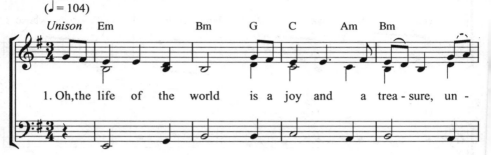

1. Oh, the life of the world is a joy and a trea - sure, un -

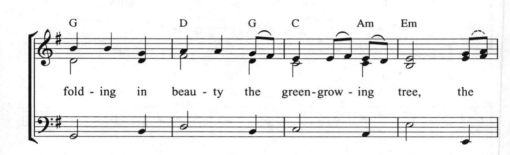

fold - ing in beau - ty the green-grow - ing tree, the

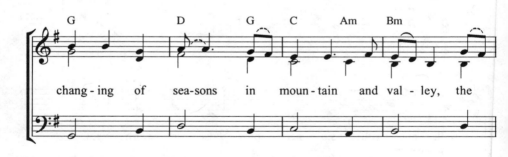

chang - ing of sea - sons in moun - tain and val - ley, the

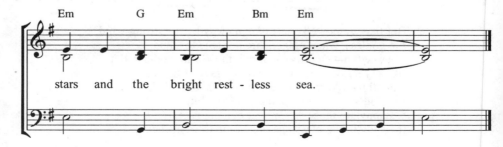

stars and the bright rest - less sea.

2. Oh, the life of the world is a fountain of goodness
   overflowing in labour and passion and pain,
   in the sound of the city and the silence of wisdom,
   in the birth of a child once again.

3. Oh, the life of the world is the source of our healing,
   it rises in laughter and wells up in song;
   it springs from the care of the poor and the broken
   and refreshes where justice is strong.

4. So give thanks for the life and give love to the maker,
   and rejoice in the gift of the bright risen Son,
   and walk in the peace and the power of the Spirit
   till the days of our living are done.

146 O land of love

Anthem for Ireland

Desmond Leslie

Traditional Irish melody
arr. Keith Duke

DANNY BOY 11 10 11 10 11 10 11 12

O land of love, we bless thee, gen-tle mo - ther; O land of light, fair jew - el of the sea. O land of joy, where {bro-ther shall greet bro - ther, / sis - ter shall greet sis - ter,} and all thy souls shall dwell in har-mo - ny. And when the

2. All wounds shall heal, unkindness be forgiven;
   all hurts forgot, as ends our darkest night.
   No more shall we by war nor strife be riven:
   all Ireland's* children face the future bright.
   One God shall reign in hearts his flame has lighted,
   and he shall lead our people to the sun.
   One heart, one soul, one land by love united,
   where we shall live in peace until this world be done.

Or 'this land's'

147 O let us spread the pollen of peace

Roger Courtney

Roger Courtney
arr. Keith Duke

O let us spread the pol-len of peace through-out our land, let us spread the pol-len of peace through-out our land; let us spread the pol-len of peace and make all con-flict

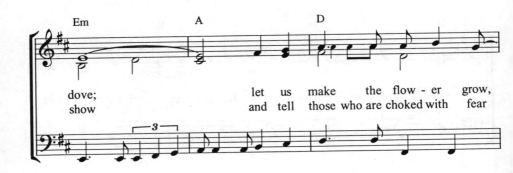

dove;   let us make   the flow - er   grow,
show   and tell those who are choked with   fear

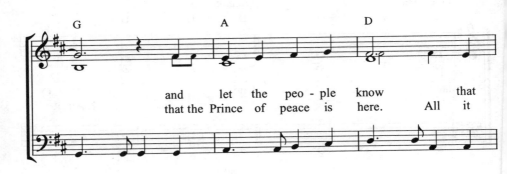

and   let   the peo - ple know   that
that the Prince of peace is   here.   All   it

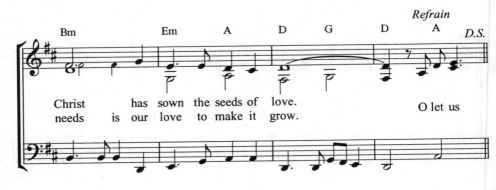

Christ   has sown the seeds of love.
needs   is our love to make it grow.   O let us

CELTIC
HYMN BOOK

148 One bread, one body

John Foley, based on 1 Corinthians 10:16, 17; 12:4;
Galatians 3:28; Didaché 9

John Foley

One bread, one bo-dy, one Lord of

all, one cup of bles-sing which we bless.

And we though ma-ny,

through-out the earth, we are one

2. Grain for the fields,
   scattered and grown,
   gathered to one, for all.

CELTIC
HYMN BOOK

149 One is the Body

John L. Bell
based on Ephesians 4:11-16

John L. Bell

PEACOCK 10 10 12

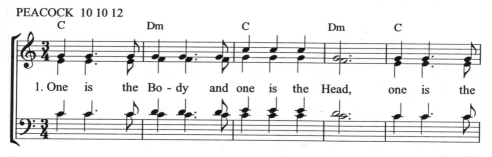

1. One is the Bo-dy and one is the Head, one is the

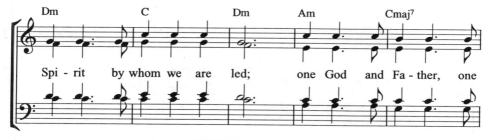

Spi-rit by whom we are led; one God and Fa-ther, one

To next verse   *Last time*

faith and one call for all. Christ our Lord.

2. Christ who ascended to heaven above
   is the same Jesus whose nature is love,
   who once descended
   to bring to this earth new birth.

3. Gifts have been given well suited to each;
   some to be prophets, to pastor or preach,
   some, through the Gospel,
   to challenge, convert and teach.

4. Called to his service are women and men
   so that his body might ever again
   witness through worship,
   through deed and through word
   to Christ our Lord.

150 Only you, Lord, can make us whole

David Adam   Rosemary Turnbull

151 On the holy cross I see

Unknown

Keith Duke

On the ho - ly cross I see Je - sus' hands nailed fast for me;

on the ho - ly cross I see Je - sus' hands nailed fast for me.

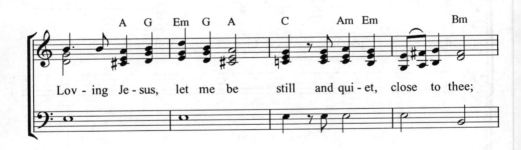

Lov - ing Je - sus, let me be still and qui - et, close to thee;

learn - ing all thy love for me, giv - ing all my love to thee.

152 Open my eyes

Sensing the presence

David Adam

NORA WITH THE PURSE 89 8 10 88 89

Traditional Irish melody
adapted by Jacynth Hamill
arr. Keith Duke

CELTIC
HYMN BOOK

153 Open my eyes that I may see

David Adam

Keith Duke

(♩ = 88)

Unison

1. O-pen my eyes that I may see the pre - sence that is all a-bout me. O-pen my ears that I may hear the voice that is quiet, yet e - ver near.

2. Open my heart that I may feel
   the love of my God, close and real.
   Open each sense, make me aware
   of the power and peace always there.

154 O praise him!

Arthur Scholey

Donald Swann
arr. Keith Duke

THE SONG OF CAEDMON

($\quad$ = 140)

Unison

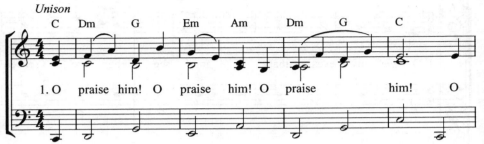

1. O praise him! O praise him! O praise him! O

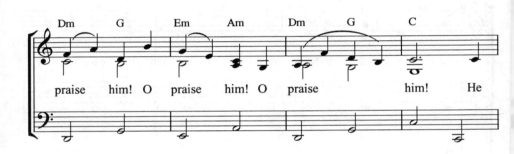

praise him! O praise him! O praise him! He

made the heav'ns, he made our sky, the sun, the moon, the stars on high; he

formed our world; his migh-ty hand di - vi - ded sea and

land: he moves in wind and rain and snow, his life is in all things that grow: O praise him! O praise him! O praise him! O praise him!

2. O praise him! O praise him! O praise him!
O praise him! O praise him! O praise him!
His joy is in the eagle's flight,
the tiger's roar, the lion's might,
the lamb, the python and the whale,
the spider, ant and snail;
all things that leap and swim and fly
on land and sea and in the sky,
they praise him, they praise him, they praise him.

3. O praise him! O praise him! O praise him!
O praise him! O praise him! O praise him!
He lives his life in love and joy,
in man and woman, girl and boy;
his purpose is in me and you,
in what we are and do;
his love is in us when we sing
with ev'ry God-created thing,
and praise him, and praise him, and praise him.

155 Our walk this day with God

Carmina Gadelica

Traditional Breton hymn
arr. Keith Duke

SANTEZ MARI 66 76 96

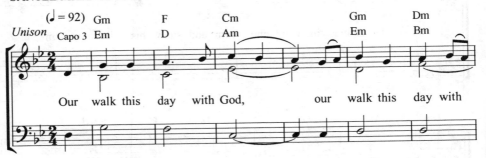

Our walk this day with God, our walk this day with

Christ, our walk this day with Spi - rit in

mer - cy, truth and peace. Our walk this day with the

Three of grace in mer - cy, truth and peace.

156 Over fields of green

Joanne Hogg

Keith Getty
arr. Keith Duke

Unison (♩. = 144)

1. O - ver fields of green from north to south a - cross the sea of blue, let the joy of such cre - a - tive pow'r re - lease our song to you U - ni - ted by your pro - mise so faith - ful and so true, as your Spi - rit soars with - in our hearts our song shall rise to you, our song shall rise to you.

2. So may the music of our song
   release a healing pow'r,
   and with all God's angels join our hearts
   in heaven's song above.

CELTIC
HYMN BOOK

157 Praise is due to you

Ray Simpson

Ray Simpson
arr. Keith Duke

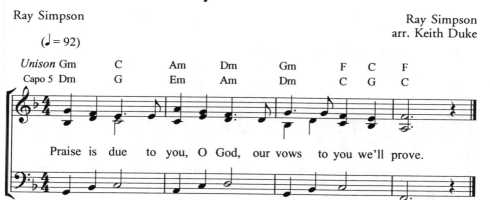

Praise is due to you, O God, our vows to you we'll prove.

158 Praise to the Lord

World without end

John L. Bell
Graham Maule

Traditional Scottish melody
arr. Keith Duke

BONNIE GEORGE CAMPBELL 10 10 10 10

1. Praise to the Lord for the joys of the earth: cy-cles of sea-son and rea-son and birth, con-trasts in out-look and land-scape and need, chal-lenge of fa-mine, pol-lu-tion and greed.

2. Praise to the Lord for the progress of life:
cradle and grave, bond of husband and wife,
pain of youth growing and wrinkling of age,
questions in step with experience and stage.

3. Praise to the Lord for the care of our kind:
faith for the faithless and sight for the blind,
healing, acceptance, disturbance and change,
all the emotions through which our lives range.

4. Praise to the Lord for the people we meet,
   safe in our homes or at risk in the street;
   kiss of a lover and friendship's embrace,
   smile of a stranger and words full of grace.

5. Praise to the Lord for the carpenter's son,
   dovetailing worship and work into one:
   tradesman and teacher and vagrant and friend,
   source of all life in this world without end.

159 Praise to you

Roc O'Connor

Roc O'Connor

Praise to you, Lord Je-sus Christ,

King of end-less glo-ry.

160 Proud, yet humble *Saint Aidan of Lindisfarne*

Edwin Le Grice

Traditional Warwickshire ballad
arr. Keith Duke

SHIPSTON 87 87

1. Proud, yet hum-ble, strong and gen-tle, from I-o-na's
ho-ly shore Ai-dan to King Os-wald's prince-dom
Christ-ian joy and ra-diance bore.

2. Where the ruthless zeal of others
quenched the smould'ring flax of love,
Aidan warmed the coldest spirits
with the fire from heav'n above.

3. At the quest of Kings and rulers
seated at the royal right hand
Aidan shared both food and silver
with the poorest of the land.

4. Staff in hand Christ's shepherd journeyed
over northern dale and moor
bringing vision, faith and friendship
to the outcast and the poor.

5. Lindisfarne, his Holy Island,
wild, yet tranquil, windswept, fair,
nurtured in severe seclusion
northern saints and folk of pray'r.

6. Cuthbert, Cedd and Chad and Hilda,
folk of courage, faith and fire,
bright with Aidan's celtic vision
still today our lives inspire.

7. In the joy of God the Spirit
to the Lord of all we bring
praise for folk of northern England,
servant saints of Christ the King.

161 Put peace into each other's hands

Fred Kaan

Irish melody from the *Petrie Collection*
arr. Keith Duke

ST COLUMBA 87 87

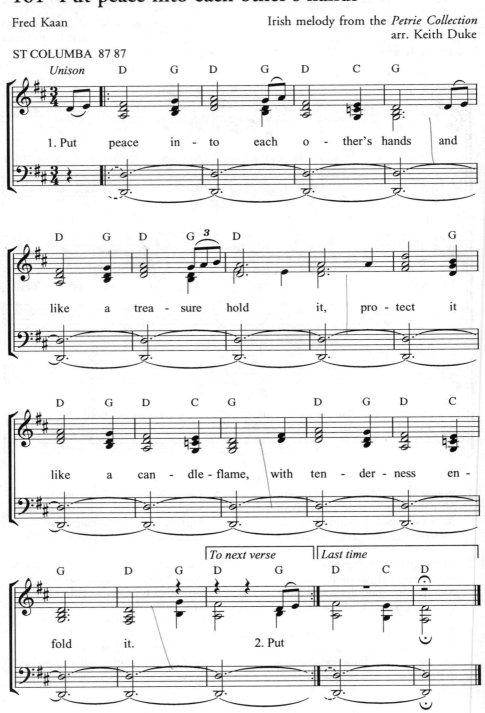

1. Put peace in-to each o-ther's hands and
like a trea-sure hold it, pro-tect it
like a can-dle-flame, with ten-der-ness en-
fold it.

To next verse | *Last time*

2. Put

2. Put peace into each other's hands
   with loving expectation;
   be gentle in your words and ways,
   in touch with God's creation.

3. Put peace into each other's hands
   like bread we break for sharing;
   look people warmly in the eye:
   our life is meant for caring.

4. As at communion, shape your hands
   into a waiting cradle;
   the gift of Christ receive, revere,
   united round the table.

5. Put Christ into each other's hands,
   he is love's deepest measure;
   in love make peace, give peace a chance
   and share it like a treasure.

162 Saint Cuthbert was a very funny man

Unknown, collected by
Ray Simpson

Unknown
arr. Keith Duke

Saint Cuth - bert was a ve - ry fun - ny man, and a
ve-ry fun-ny man was he. He wad - ed out in the
mid-dle of the night and stood in the cold wet sea; yes,
stood in the cold wet sea. 1. He sang to God for a
long, long time to the sounds of the birds and the

sea. He did - n't catch a cold which was

ve - ry ve - ry odd. Oh, a ve - ry fun - ny man was

he; yes, a ve - ry fun - ny man was he.

2. When morning came he returned to the beach
   and kneeled on the sand to pray.
   Two otters came and rolled around his feet
   in a very very friendly way;
   yes, a very very friendly way.

3. If you could meet this very funny man
   who lived many many years ago
   what questions would you ask? What answers would he give?
   I would very much like to know;
   yes, I would very much like to know.

163 Saintly Aidan, priest of heaven

Richard H. Noxon

Tom P. Anderson
arr. Keith Duke

SAINTLY AIDAN 87 87

(♩ = 100)

Saint-ly Ai-dan, priest of hea-ven, saint - ly Ai-dan, priest of God: self-less-ly his life was giv-en her - ald-ing the ho - ly word.

2. At the Father's call compelling
   to Iona's shores he came,
   heart with Christian fervour swelling,
   soul with Christian fire aflame.

3. Oswald for his aid beseeching,
   Aidan to Northumbria trod,
   swayed the heathen with his teaching
   of the promised land of God.

4. Ever onward through the nation
   faith-impelled he laboured on;
   converts thronged in exultation
   by his stirring message drawn.

5. Praise to Aidan, all-inspiring,
   servant of the Father's will.
   May we likewise toil untiring
   Christian duty to fulfil.

164 Saint of the Spirit's quest

Saint Cuthbert

Edwin Le Grice

Melody from Madan's *Collection* (1769)
arr. Keith Duke

MOSCOW 664 6664

(♩ = 104)

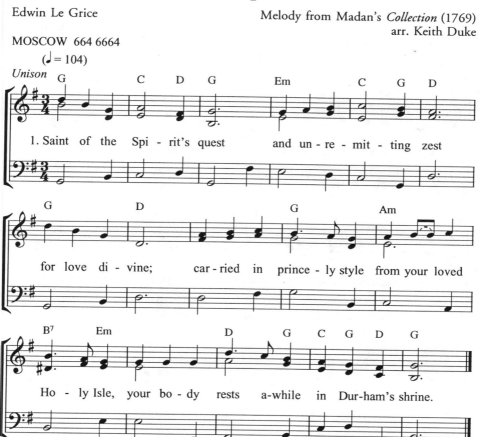

1. Saint of the Spi - rit's quest and un - re - mit - ting zest for love di - vine; car - ried in prince - ly style from your loved Ho - ly Isle, your bo - dy rests a - while in Dur-ham's shrine.

2. Monk of the open hand –
   for Ripon's Melrose band
   keeping the door;
   off'ring a needed bed
   to many a traveller's head,
   sharing your wine and bread
   with Christ's own poor.

3. Cuthbert, the otters' friend –
   but first, to your life's end
   God's pray'rful priest.
   From storm-swept island lair
   teaching us all to share
   the great Creator's care
   for man and beast.

4. Help us, good Northern Saint
   to pray, and not to faint,
   as once before
   on Lindisfarne's rough land
   with Aidan's crook in hand
   you taught your pilgrim band
   how to adore.

165 Saints of the Isles, rejoice

Ray Simpson

Martin Shaw
arr. Keith Duke

LITTLE CORNARD 66 66 88

1. Saints of the Isles, re-joice, Bri-gid and Co-lum-cille, com-pas-sion's trou-ba-dours, you trod our fra-gile soil. From Pat-rick's Mount to Bren-dan's Bay you plumbed our depths and shared our toil. cries.

To next verse / Last time

2. Saints of the North, take heart;
Aidan and Mother Hild,
friends of the Servant Christ,
fierce warring souls you stilled.
From Holy Isle to Thames-side shore
folk's minds you stirred, their hearts you filled.

3. Saints of the West, be glad;
David and Non uprise,
Illtyd and Samson too,
founders and teachers wise.
From Holywell to Bardsey Isle
their holy pray'r to heaven cries.

166 Saviour of my soul

David Adam

Keith Duke

This may be sung as a round, with entries as indicated

CELTIC
HYMN BOOK

167 Shelter us

Ray Simpson

Traditional Scottish melody
arr. Keith Duke

168 Sing for God's glory

Kathy Galloway

From *Praxis Pietatis Melica*
arr. Keith Duke

LOBE DEN HERREN 14 14 11 8

1. Sing for God's glo-ry that col-ours the dawn of cre-a-tion, rac-ing a-cross the sky, trail-ing bright clouds of e-la-tion; sun of de-light suc-ceeds the vel-vet of night, warm-ing the earth's ex-ul-ta-tion.

2. Sing for God's power
   that shatters the chains that would bind us,
   searing the darkness of
   fear and despair that could blind us,
   touching our shame with love that will not lay blame,
   reaching out gently to find us.

3. Sing for God's justice
   disturbing each easy illusion,
   tearing down tyrants
   and putting our pride to confusion;
   lifeblood of right, resisting evil and slight,
   offering freedom's transfusion.

4. Sing for God's saints who have
   travelled faith's journey before us,
   who in our weariness
   give us their hope to restore us;
   in them we see the new creation to be,
   spirit of love made flesh for us.

169 Sing glory to God

Michael Forster
based on the *Gloria*

Traditional Welsh melody
arr. Keith Duke

THE ASH GROVE 12 11 12 11 and Refrain

2. Lord Jesus, the Christ, only Son of the Father,
   the Lamb who has carried our burden of shame,
   now seated on high in the glory of heaven,
   have mercy upon us who call on your name.

3. For you, only you, we acknowledge as holy,
   we name you alone as our Saviour and Lord;
   you only, O Christ, with the Spirit exalted,
   at one with the Father, for ever adored.

170 Sing praise to Wisdom

Colin Hodgetts

From *Praxis Pietatis Melica* (1668)
arr. Keith Duke

LOBE DEN HERREN 14 14 11 8

1. Sing praise to Wis-dom, all gen-tle, the heart of cre-a-tion; O my soul, praise her, for she is your soul's li-be-ra-tion; all you who hear now to this foun-tain draw near; praise her with glad a-do-ra-tion.

2. Sing praise to Wisdom, the priceless, so silently reigning.
   She hides you under her wings and is gently sustaining.
   Have you not seen
   how your heart's longings have been
   granted in all her ordaining?

3. Sing praise to Wisdom, who'll nurture your work and defend you.
   Surely her strength and her insight will daily attend you.
   Hear Wisdom call.
   If you love her above all
   she in her love will befriend you.

CELTIC
HYMN BOOK

171 Source of all, we worship you

Ray Simpson

Andrew Wright

2. Pow'r of all, we honour you.
   Light of all, we honour you.
   Life of all, we honour you.

3. Ground of all, we rest in you.
   Bond of all, we rest in you.
   Friend of all, we rest in you.

172 Spirit of God, come dwell within me

Mallaig Sprinkling Song

Helen Kennedy

Traditional Scottish melody
arr. Keith Duke

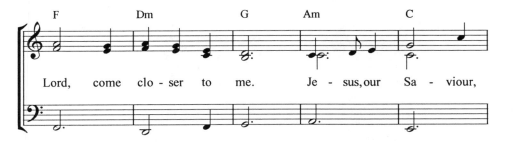

Lord, come clo - ser to me. Je - sus, our Sa - viour,

dy - ing for me, and ris - ing to save his peo - ple.

2. Lord, how I thirst, O Lord, I am weak.
Lord, come to me, you alone do I seek.
Lord, you are life, and love and hope,
O fill me with living water.

3. Lord, I am blind, O Lord, I can't see.
Stretch out your hand, O Lord, comfort me.
Lead me your way in light and in truth,
O fill me with living water.

CELTIC
HYMN BOOK

173 Spirit of God, renew the face of the earth

Ray Simpson

Keith Duke

This may be sung as a round, with entries as indicated

174 Spirit of God, unseen as the wind

Margaret Old

Traditional Scottish melody
and Annie McLeod
arr. Keith Duke

2. Without your help we fail our Lord,
   we cannot live his way;
   we need your pow'r, we need your strength,
   following Christ each day.

175 Still the harp in abbey stall   *Caedmon's Song*

C. Artley

S.E. Maltby
arr. Keith Duke

(♩ = 100)

Unison F ... C Dm C F
Capo 5 C ... G Am G C

1. Still the harp in ab - bey stall, tied the tongue of

E⁷ Am B♭ F Dm Am
B⁷ Em F C Am Em

ear - ly praise; Caed - mon heard the spi - rit's call,

Dm C F B♭ F
Am G C F C

cliff - top wind in sax - on days. Caed-mon's song now

B♭ A Dm C F B♭ F
F E Am G C F C

let us sing, prai - ses to the heav'n - ly King.

2. Hiding in the lonely byre,
   searching fingers plucked the string.
   Kindled by the spirit's fire,
   loosened tongue God's work to sing.
   Caedmon's song now let us sing,
   praise for ev'ry wondrous thing.

3. Eyes downcast to earth and hoof
   lifted to the seabird's flight.
   Soared above to heaven's roof
   saw anew with poet's sight.
   Caedmon's song now let us sing,
   praise we the almighty King.

4. He who saw in all creation
   thoughts of the creator's mind,
   gave to God his adoration,
   guardian of all humankind.
   Caedmon's song now let us sing,
   praise for ev'ry wondrous thing.

5. Give us, Lord, a searching mind,
   open to your heav'nly will.
   In our lives your purpose find;
   all our days with praises fill.
   Caedmon's song now let us sing,
   praises to the heav'nly King.

176 Teach me, dear Lord

Martin E. Leckebusch

Dick Farrelly
arr. Keith Duke

THE ISLE OF INNISFREE 11 10 11 10 11 10 11 12

1. Teach me, dear Lord, to sa-vour ev-'ry mo - ment — each pre-cious hour, a gift which is u - nique — for your un - hur - ried guid-ing hand I che - rish and the con - tent - ment of your ways I seek. When date and

time   de-mand my full at - ten - tion,   from fran - tic

rush - ing let my heart be free,   that I may

flow   with - in your Spi - rit's rhy - thm   and live each

mi - nute just as it was meant to be.

2. But may I also glimpse the broader canvas –
    to all my life, a purpose and a plan –
    and let me hear again that voice which called me
    before this world or time itself began.
    So may your kingdom daily be my watchword
    and may the pulse in all my life be praise,
    across unfolding years and changing seasons,
    until with you I walk through everlasting days.

177 Thanks for the fellowship

Jean Holloway

Traditional Scottish melody
and Annie McLeod
arr. Keith Duke

SKYE BOAT SONG 10 6 10 6 86 86 10 6 10 6

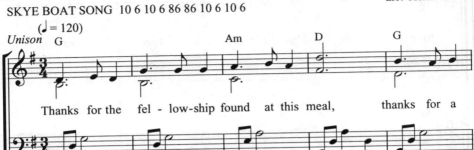

Thanks for the fel - low-ship found at this meal, thanks for a

day re - freshed; thanks to the Lord for his

pre - sence we feel, thanks for the food he blessed.

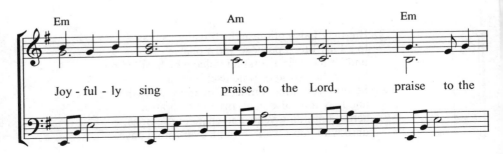

Joy - ful - ly sing praise to the Lord, praise to the

CELTIC
HYMN BOOK

178 The church is wherever God's people

Carol R. Ikeler

Traditional Irish melody
arr. Keith Duke

THE BARD OF ARMAGH 12 10 12 11

1. The church is wher-e-ver God's peo-ple are prais-ing, sing-ing their thanks for his good-ness this day. The church is wher-e-ver dis-ci-ples of Je-sus re-mem-ber his sto-ry and walk in his way.

2. The church is wherever God's people are helping,
caring for neighbours in sickness and need.
The church is wherever God's people are sharing
the words of the Bible in gift and in deed.

179 The day of the Lord shall come

John L. Bell
Graham Maule

Traditional Scottish melody
arr. Keith Duke

AIR FALALALO Irregular

1. The day of the Lord shall come, as pro-phets have told, when Christ shall make all things new, no mat-ter how old. And some at the stars may gaze, and some at God's word, in vain to pre-dict the time, the day of the Lord.

Refrain: The de-sert shall spring to life, the hills shall re-joice; the lame of the earth shall leap, the dumb shall find voice; the lamb with the lion shall lie, and the last shall be first; and na-tions for war no more shall stu-dy or thirst.

2. The day of the Lord shall come – a thief in the night,
   a curse to those in the wrong who think themselves right,
   a pleasure for those in pain or with death at the door;
   a true liberation for the pris'ners and poor.

3. The day of the Lord shall come and judgement be known,
   as nations like sheep and goats come close to the throne.
   Then Christ shall himself reveal, asking all to draw near
   and see in his face all faces once ignored here.

4. The day of the Lord shall come, but now is the time
   to subvert earth's wisdom with Christ's folly sublime,
   by loving the loveless, turning the tide and the cheek,
   by walking beneath the cross in step with the weak.

180 The eye of the God

Ray Simpson

Keith Duke

181 The Lord's my Shepherd

Psalm 23

Sammy Horner
arr. Keith Duke

Unison

1. The Lord's my Shep - herd, I'll not want, he makes me down to lie in pas - tures green, he lead - eth me the qui - et wa - ters by.

2. My soul he doth restore again,
   and me to walk doth make
   within the paths of righteousness,
   e'en for his own name's sake.

3. Yea, though I walk in death's dark vale,
   yet will I fear no ill.
   For thou art with me, and thy rod
   and staff me comfort still.

4. My table thou hast furnishèd
   in presence of my foes,
   my head thou dost with oil anoint,
   and my cup overflows.

5. Goodness and mercy all my life
   shall surely follow me.
   And in God's house for evermore
   my dwelling-place shall be.

182 The love of Christ surround us *Christ with us*

David Adam

Rosemary Turnbull
arr. Keith Duke

183 The love of God

David Adam

Keith Duke

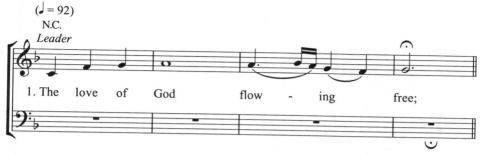

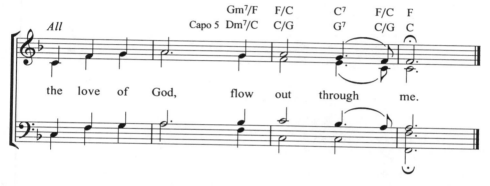

2. The peace of God . . .

3. The breath of God . . .

4. The strength of God . . .

5. The life of God . . .

Alternative verses:

The pow'r of God . . .

The calm of God . . .

The bliss of God . . .

The rest of God . . .

The light of God . . .

The health of God . . .

The hand of God . . .

The grace of God . . .

The heart of God . . .

The joy of God . . .

The presence of God . . .

The mind of God . . .

CELTIC
HYMN BOOK

184 The peace of the earth

Guatamalan
trans. Christine Carson

Guatamalan folk melody
arr. Keith Duke

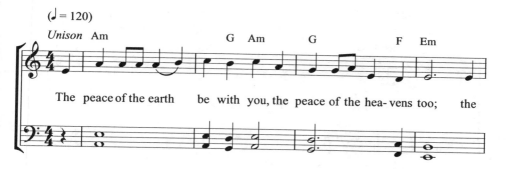

The peace of the earth be with you, the peace of the hea-vens too; the

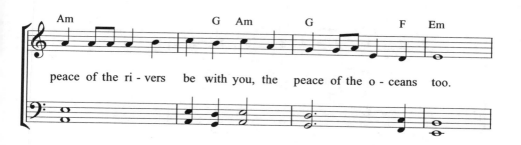

peace of the ri - vers be with you, the peace of the o - ceans too.

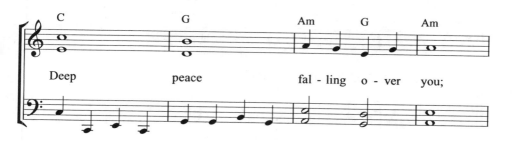

Deep peace fal - ling o - ver you;

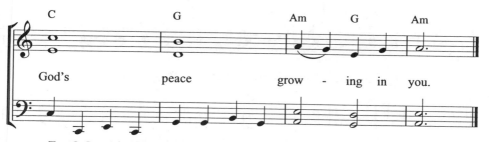

God's peace grow - ing in you.

185 There's a life after this

Sammy Horner

Sammy Horner
arr. Keith Duke

Lyrics:
There's a life af-ter this, and the saints will go to hea-ven, and they'll serve the Lord of glo-ry there; there's a life af-ter this. There's a this. this.

1. Why do the wic-ked pros-per? Why do they gain?

2. Why do the righteous struggle?
   Why do they fail?
   Why do they strive so hard,
   and still they look so frail?
   Help us take courage, Lord,
   and take us by the hand,
   and guide us by your words
   to the glory of your promised land.

186 The shape of Christ be with me

Taladh Chriosda

Carmina Gadelica

Traditional Gaelic melody
arr. Keith Duke

1. The shape of Christ be with me, the shape of Christ be-fore me, the shape of Christ be-hind me on Sun-day and on Mon-day.

2. The shape of Christ be over me,
   the shape of Christ be under me,
   the shape of Christ around me
   on Tuesday and on Wednesday.

3. The shape of Christ be with me,
   before me, behind me,
   within me, around me
   on Thursday, Friday, Saturday.

4. Alleluia, alleluia,
   alleluia, alleluia,
   alleluia, alleluia,
   alleluia, alleluia.

187 The tide ebbs

David Adam

Tide change

Keith Duke

The tide ebbs; dark-ness will come;
draw me, Lord, to your home.
The waves are high; the storms in-crease;
draw me, Lord, to your peace.

188 This day God gives me

St Patrick's Breastplate
adapted by James Quinn

Traditional Gaelic melody
arr. Keith Duke

BUNESSAN 55 54 D

1. This day God gives me strength of high hea - ven,
sun and moon shin - ing, flame in my hearth;
flash-ing of light - ning, wind in its swift - ness,
deeps of the o - cean, firm-ness of earth.

2. This day God sends me
   strength to sustain me,
   might to uphold me,
   wisdom as guide.
   Your eyes are watchful,
   your ears are list'ning,
   your lips are speaking,
   friend at my side.

3. God's way is my way,
   God's shield is round me,
   God's host defends me,
   saving from ill.
   Angel of heaven,
   drive from me always
   all that would harm me,
   stand by me still.

4. Rising, I thank you,
   mighty and strong One,
   King of creation,
   giver of rest,
   firmly confessing
   Threeness of persons,
   Oneness of Godhead,
   Trinity blest.

189 This fragile vessel

Máire Brennan

Keith Getty
arr. Keith Duke

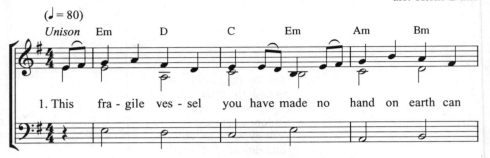

1. This fra-gile ves-sel you have made no hand on earth can

fill, for the wa-ters of this world have failed, and

I am thir-sty still. *Refrain* We can be wor-thy of his love,

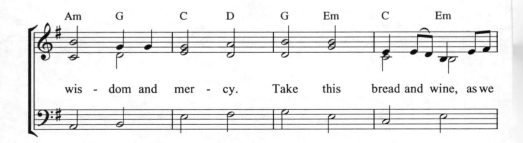

wis - dom and mer - cy. Take this bread and wine, as we

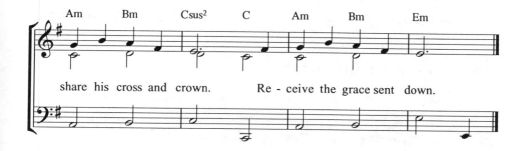

share his cross and crown. Re - ceive the grace sent down.

2. I seek the treasures of your love,
   it's not that far to see.
   I heard a melody above;
   a gift from you to me.

3. To save what's lost from heav'n he came,
   his presence still remain.
   Open our eyes to his precious blood,
   because it's not in vain.

190 Those who live in God's own shelter

Margaret Harvey
based on Psalm 91

Thomas Williams
arr. Keith Duke

EBENEZER (TON-Y-BOTEL) 87 87 D

1. Those who live in God's own shel-ter, in his sha-dow

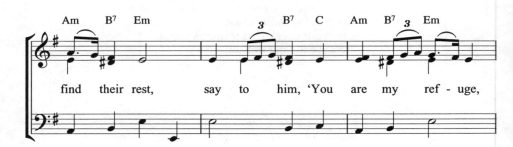

find their rest, say to him, 'You are my ref-uge,

God, in whom I put my trust.' He will keep you

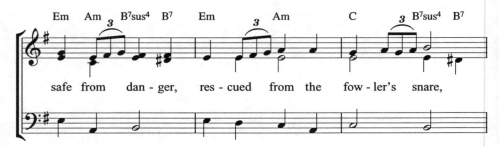

safe from dan-ger, res-cued from the fow-ler's snare,

he will spread his great wings o - ver you,

you'll find safe - ty in his care.

2. With his truth as shield and buckler
   no night terrors shall you fear,
   daytime's arrows shall not pierce you,
   plague nor evil shall come near;
   though a thousand fall beside you
   thousands fall at your right hand,
   though you look with fear and wonder
   yet with God secure you'll stand.

3. When you make God your defender
   evil shall not touch your home,
   angels keep their guard about you
   lest you fall against a stone,
   you shall tread upon the serpent
   lions trample underfoot;
   when you call, then God will answer,
   he will fill your life with good.

191 Though I am just an ignorant child

Sammy Horner

Sammy Horner
arr. Keith Duke

Lyrics:

1. Though I am just an ig-no-rant child, you are a friend to me. And though you are the migh-ty one, my friend you wish to be. And e-ven though my eyes are dim, my heart filled

2. I see in lives of others your grace and mercy sweet.
   Your hand is often guiding the other folk I meet.
   And in your book I read the words and though not always clear,
   you show your mercy helping me to see, and touch and hear.

3. So in the world around me I hear your praises ring.
   The wind, the sea, the summer rain, the birds that love to sing.
   I see in ev'ry sunrise your presence with us here,
   and so at least in measure I can see, and touch and hear.

192 Three seams in this garment

Sammy Horner

Sammy Horner
arr. Keith Duke

1. Three seams in this gar-ment, one gar-ment I wear; three

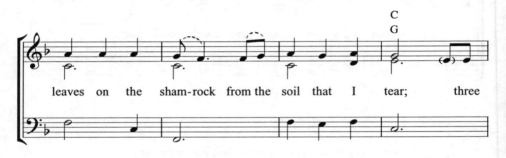

leaves on the sham-rock from the soil that I tear; three

joints in my fin-ger, yet one fin-ger there; blessed

Fa-ther, Son, Spi-rit, yet one God I serve. The

three are the one, and the one is the three; blessed

Fa - ther, Son, Spi - rit, blessed Tri - ni - ty.

2. She's a wife and a mother and a daughter in one;
   he's a father, a husband and also a son;
   and the water can be the stream or the snow;
   blessed Father, Son, Spirit, yet one God I know.

3. Now no tongue can tell, no language explain
   the greatness of God or his fulness of being;
   and though it remains a great mystery,
   you're a Father, a Saviour and a comfort to me.

193 Through the love of God our Saviour

M. Peters

Traditional Welsh melody
arr. Keith Duke

AR HYD Y NOS 84 84 88 84

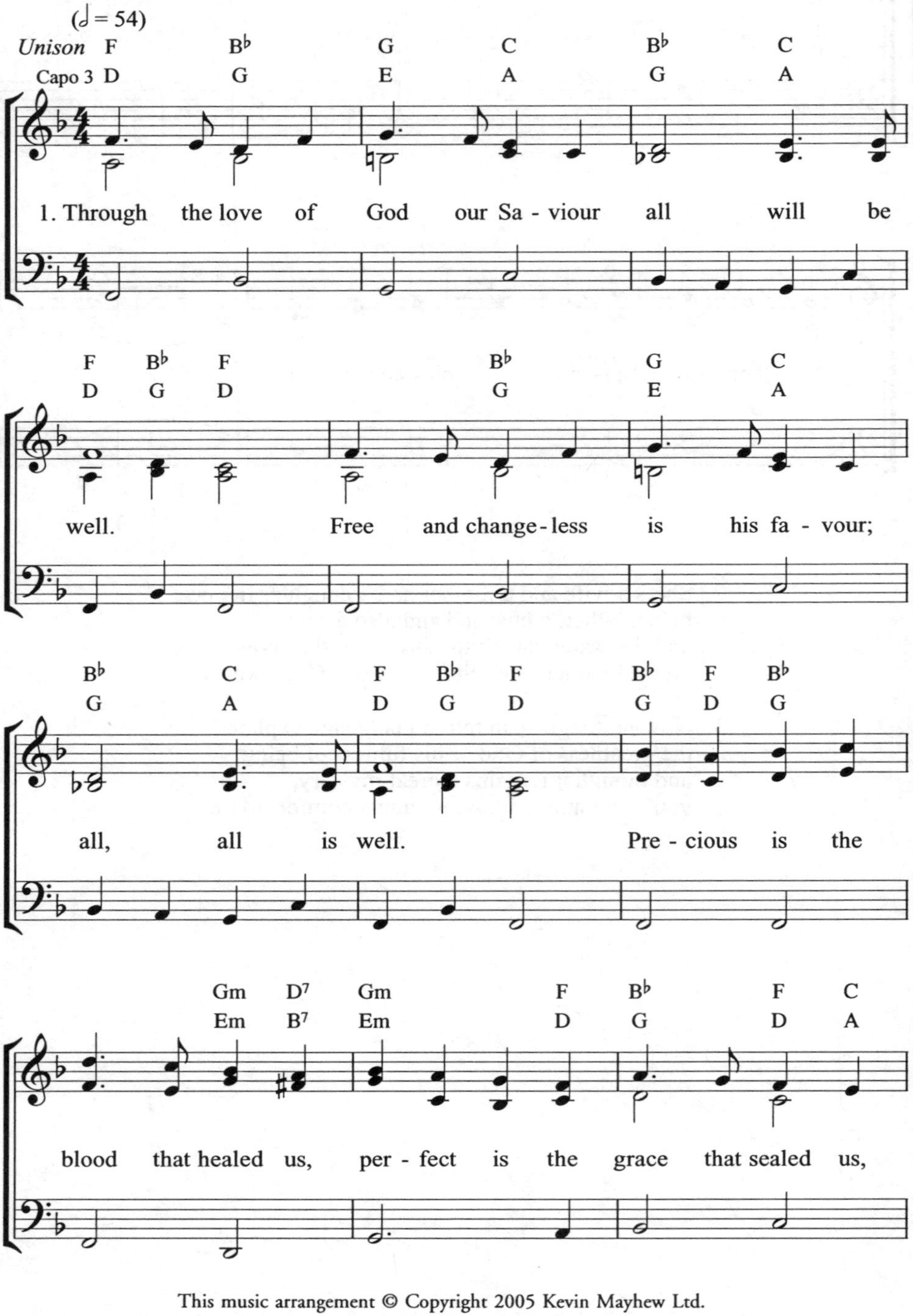

(𝅗𝅥 = 54)
Unison
F B♭ G C B♭ C
Capo 3 D G E A G A
1. Through the love of God our Sa - viour all will be
F B♭ F B♭ G C
D G D G E A
well. Free and change - less is his fa - vour;
B♭ C F B♭ F B♭ F B♭
G A D G D G D G
all, all is well. Pre - cious is the
Gm D7 Gm F B♭ F C
Em B7 Em D G D A
blood that healed us, per - fect is the grace that sealed us,

strong the hand stretched forth to shield us; all must be well.

2. Though we pass through tribulation,
   all will be well.
   Ours is such a full salvation,
   all, all is well.
   Happy still in God confiding,
   fruitful, if in Christ abiding,
   holy, through the Spirit's guiding;
   all must be well.

3. We expect a bright tomorrow;
   all will be well.
   Faith can sing through days of sorrow,
   'All, all is well.'
   On our Father's love relying,
   Jesus ev'ry need supplying,
   or in living or in dying,
   all must be well.

194 Thuma mina

Send me, Lord

Traditional South African

Traditional South African melody
arr. Keith Duke

1. Thu-ma mi-na, thu-ma mi-na, thu-ma mi-na, So-man-dla.
   Je-sus, send me, Je-sus, send me, Je-sus, send me, Lord.

2. Send me, Lord.
   Send me, Jesus *(x3)*
   Send me, Lord.

3. Lead me, Lord.
   Lead me, Jesus *(x3)*
   Lead me, Lord.

4. Fill me, Lord.
   Fill me, Jesus *(x3)*
   Fill me, Lord.

5. Thuma mina . . .

195 To the Creator who gives you life

David Adam

Keith Duke

(♩ = 60)

To the Cre - a-tor who gives you life, we give your
life. To the Sa-viour who gives love, we give you in
love. To the Spi-rit who gives him-self, we give you to
him. In the pow-er, peace and pre-sence of Fa-ther,
Son and Ho-ly Spi - rit, we im - merse you to-day.

196 To the Sun of suns come singing

Ray Simpson

Traditional melody
arr. Keith Duke

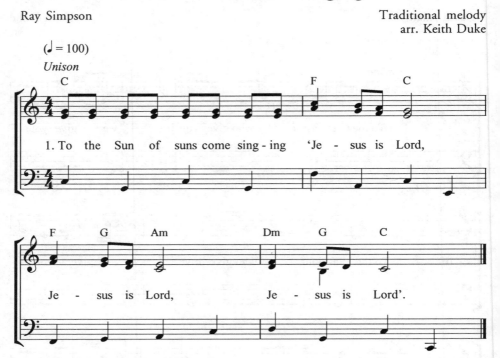

($\downarrow$ = 100)

Unison

1. To the Sun of suns come sing-ing 'Je - sus is Lord,
Je - sus is Lord, Je - sus is Lord'.

2. Earth come to the sun's King singing 'Jesus is Lord,
   Jesus is Lord, Jesus is Lord'.

3. Sky come to the sun's King singing 'Jesus is Lord,
   Jesus is Lord, Jesus is Lord'.

4. Spirits come to sun's King singing 'Jesus is Lord,
   Jesus is Lord, Jesus is Lord'.

5. Father, Saviour, lighting Spirit, you are the Lord,
   you are the Lord, you are the Lord.

197 Touch the earth lightly

Shirley Erena Murray

Colin Gibson
arr. Keith Duke

TENDERNESS 10 10 10 10

2. We who endanger, who create hunger,
   agents of death for all creatures that live,
   we who would foster clouds of disaster,
   God of our planet, forestall and forgive!

3. Let there be greening, birth from the burning,
   water that blesses and air that is sweet,
   health in God's garden, hope in God's children,
   regeneration that peace will complete.

4. God of all living, God of all loving,
   God of the seedling, the snow and the sun,
   teach us, deflect us, Christ reconnect us,
   using us gently and making us one.

CELTIC
HYMN BOOK

198 Trim the cruisie's failing light

Rune of Barra
trans. Murdoch MacLean

John L. Bell

2. Lift the sneck and wooden bar
   and leave the stranger's door ajar
   lest he may tarry lowly,
   the Son of Mary holy.

3. Sweep the hearth and pile the peat
   and set the board with bread and meat;
   the Son of God may take it,
   the Son of Mary break it.

199 We are marching in the light of God

Traditional South African hymn
trans. Anders Nyberg

Traditional South African melody
arr. Keith Duke

SIYAHAMBA 99 99 10 10 10 10

1. We are march - ing in the light of God, we are

march-ing in the light of God. We are

march - ing in the light of God, we are

march-ing in the light of God. We are

2. We are marching in the love of God . . .

3. We are marching in the life of God . . .

200 We cannot measure how you heal

John L. Bell
Graham Maule

Traditional English melody
arr. Keith Duke

O WALY WALY 88 88

1. We can-not mea - sure how you heal or ans-wer
ev - 'ry suf-f'rer's prayer, yet we be - lieve your grace res -
ponds where faith and doubt u - nite to care.

2. Your hands, though bloodied on the cross,
survive to hold and heal and warn,
to carry all through death to life
and cradle children yet unborn.

3. The pain that will not go away,
the guilt that clings from things
long past,
the fear of what the future holds,
are present as if meant to last.

4. But present too is love which tends
the hurt we never hoped to find,
the private agonies inside,
the memories that haunt the mind.

5. So some have come who need your help
and some have come to make amends,
as hands which shaped and saved
the world
are present in the touch of friends.

6. Lord, let your Spirit meet us here
to mend the body, mind and soul,
to disentangle peace from pain
and make your broken people whole.

201 We draw aside at the heart of the day

Andrew Dick

Andrew Dick
arr. Keith Duke

1. We draw aside at the heart of the day to seek your face and watch and pray. Refresh us, O Lord, and close to us stay when we leave here and each go our way.

2. As with man - na you fed your flee - ing folk like much - need - ed rain on the parched dry ground, refresh us now as your name we in - voke, we come like dew in pow'r on us now.

202 We need your mother love, O God

Garth Hewitt

Garth Hewitt
arr. Keith Duke

1. We need your mo-ther love, O God, to keep and hold us tight, we need your mo-ther love, O God, to lead us through the night. We need your Ho-ly Spi-rit to com-fort and to guide;

may she give us cou-rage · to do what's right.

2. We need your mother love, O God, to teach us how to live,
   a love that never forces but draws because it gives.
   May we reject the pride that thinks we are the best
   that we deserve much more while others can have less.

3. We need your mother love, O God, to teach us to say no
   to all the ways of violence, to all the ways of war.
   Forgive us for the way we have supported evil deeds
   done in the name of our nation while we've simply kept our peace.

4. We need your mother love, O God, to teach us to say yes
   to all the ways of beauty, to all the ways that bless,
   to be gentle with creation and all God's creatures too,
   to treat the earth with kindness, to cherish and renew.

5. We need your mother love, O God, so we're numbered with the meek;
   forgive our need to dominate over poor and weak.
   And men over women and race over race
   forgive us for the fear that hides the human face.

6. We need your mother love, O God, to keep our spirits true
   to the values of your Kingdom, to the attitudes from you.
   Blessèd are the merciful, blessèd are the meek,
   blessèd are the humble, blessèd are the weak.

   Repeat verse 1

203 We seek your presence

Paul Kyle

Paul Kyle
arr. Keith Duke

(♩ = 92)

Unison D   A   Bm
Capo 2 C   G   Am

We   seek your pre - sence.

G   D   A
F   C   G

Lord, we long   to see your face.

D   A   Bm
C   G   Am

We   seek your pre - sence.   Lord come

G   A   D
F   G   C

now,   in your mer - cy,   fill this space.

204 We shall go out with hope of resurrection

Resurrection Song

June Boyce-Tillman

Keith Duke

1. We shall go out with hope of re-sur-rec-tion; we shall go out from strength to strength go on; we shall go out and tell our sto-ries bold-ly; tales of a love that will not let us go.

2. We'll sing our songs of wrongs that can be righted;
   we'll dream our dreams of hurts that can be healed;
   we'll weave a cloth of all the world united
   within the vision of a Christ who makes us free.

3. We'll give a voice to those who have not spoken;
   we'll find the words for those whose lips are sealed;
   we'll make the tunes for those who sing no longer,
   vibrating love alive in ev'ry heart.

4. We'll share our joy with those who are still weeping,
   chant hymns of strength for hearts that break in grief;
   we'll leap and dance the resurrection story
   including all within the circles of our love.

205 We swear by peace and love

Ancient Celtic prayer

Keith Duke

We swear by peace and love to stand

heart to heart and hand in hand;

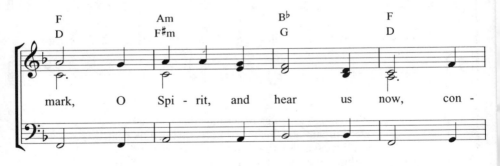

mark, O Spi - rit, and hear us now, con -

To repeat | Last time

firm - ing this our sac - red vow. vow.

206 When our steps are weary

The gate of glory

David Adam

Angela Reith
arr. Keith Duke

207 When Saxon Oswiu gave to Hild
Saint Hilda's hymn

C. Artley

S.E. Maltby

HINDERWELL 886 D

1. When Sax-on Os-wiu gave to Hild a grant of land on which to build, her ab-bey Hil-da planned. Hud-dled a-gainst the nor-thern gales in sight of sea and dis-tant dales, a-bove the shift-ing sand.

2. Like jewelled necklace blazing bright,
   in heathen darkness shedding light
   from quiet holy cell,
   where living waters met the sea,
   she spent her life in purity,
   God's faithfulness to tell.

3. Her wisdom shared in humble things
   and counsel gave to troubled kings;
   in Aidan's footsteps trod.
   Obedient to Columba's rule,
   her abbey grown, a bishop's school,
   proclaimed the word of God.

4. There man and woman equally
   in holiness and charity,
   within Saint Hild's domain.
   In simpleness apart to live
   and yet together praises give
   upon the abbey plain.

5. Grant, living Lord, that we may find
   serenity and peace of mind
   that blessèd Hilda knew.
   Amidst the storms and gales which rage
   about us in our present age,
   your life in us renew.

208 When the Church, in holy synod

Anthony Duncan

From the *Paderborn Gesangbuch* (1765)
arr. Keith Duke

DAILY DAILY 87 87 D

(♩ = 100)

1. When the Church, in ho-ly sy-nod met by Aln-mouth's san-dy shore, with King Eg-frith of North-um-bria and Arch-bi-shop The-o-dore, to ad-vance the Lord's own king-dom a-mong those who had not heard the great mes-sage of sal-va-tion or the preach-ing of the word.

2. They elected as a bishop
   once a monk of Lindisfarne,
   holy Cuthbert, now a hermit
   on the isle of Inner Farne.
   Both the King and the Archbishop
   in a ship then set their sail,
   came as pilgrims to his island
   that their wishes might prevail.

3. Holy Cuthbert then surrendered
   to God's will, though grieving sore,
   and was consecrated bishop
   by Archbishop Theodore;
   first for Hexham, then returning
   to Northumbria's Holy Isle;
   very image of his Master
   for a blessèd little while.

4. We have come, who here are gathered
   to a great inheritance;
   and the faith to us delivered
   may we never leave to chance.
   Strive we with our holy fathers
   in their prayers and by their worth,
   that the fulness of the kingdom
   may be manifest on earth.

209 When the dove cannot fly

Rainbow's end

Kenyon E. Wright

Traditional Irish melody
arr. Keith Duke

THE ROSE OF TRALEE 13 12 13 12

1. When the dove can-not fly for its oil-clot-ted pin-ions; when the
o - live branch wi - thers in soil made im - pure; when the
rain - bow cor - rodes in a rain be - come a - cid; will the
pro - mise still hold, will the earth still en-dure? If a
nu - cle - ar win - ter as - sa - si - nates spring-time; if

seed - time made bar - ren brings har - vest no more; if
day turns to dark - ness and dusk with - out dawn - ing, how
long, Lord, how long will the earth yet en - dure?

2. When the safety of some means the mis'ry of many;
   when the affluent feast on the flesh of the poor;
   when the debts must be paid through the weeping of children;
   will his mercy remain, will the earth yet endure?
   If, greedy for gain and in fear of our failure,
   we sell our tomorrows for meaningless gold,
   if the summit won't see, and earth's last chance is squandered
   will the earth yet endure, does the promise grow cold?

3. If our riches today mean our ruin tomorrow,
   if we cannot now see what belongs to our peace,
   if we're blind to God's moments of justice and mercy,
   will the earth yet endure, will his mercy now cease?
   Where the lamp of the lamb lights our guilt and our gladness:
   where the book of God's judgement at last is unsealed:
   where the clear crystal river of mercy is flowing:
   there the tree of life blossoms, the nations are healed.

210 Where the love of Christ unites us

Michael Forster

Traditonal Welsh melody
arr. Keith Duke

AR HYD Y NOS 84 84 88 84

($\boldsymbol{\downarrow}$ = 54)

1. Where the love of Christ u-nites us, there God is found. Where we meet as love in-vites us, there God is found. Let us come with ju-bi-la-tion to the God of our sal-va-tion;

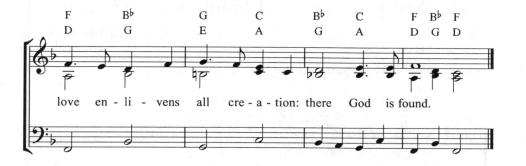

love en - li - vens all cre - a - tion: there God is found.

2. Where we meet without division,
   there God is found,
   free from anger and derision,
   there God is found.
   Let all bitter feuds be ended,
   strife resolved and foes befriended,
   pride and fear by love transcended:
   there God is found.

3. Where the blessèd live for ever,
   there God is found;
   bonds of love no pain can sever,
   there God is found.
   Christ in glory, we implore you,
   let us with the saints adore you,
   love resplendent flows before you;
   there God is found.

211 Will you come and follow me *The Summons*

John L. Bell
Graham Maule

Traditional Scottish melody
arr. Keith Duke

KELVINGROVE 76 76 77 76

1. Will you come and fol - low me if I but call your name? Will you go where you don't know and ne - ver be the same? Will you let my love be shown, will you let my name be known,

C   F   C   Dm   Bb
G   C   G   Am   F

will you let my life be grown in you and you

F
C

in me?

C
G

Dm   F   Bb   F
Am   C   F   C

2. Will you leave yourself behind
    if I but call your name?
    Will you care for cruel and kind,
    and never be the same?
    Will you risk the hostile stare
    should your life attract or scare,
    will you let me answer prayer
    in you, and you in me?

3. Will you let the blinded see
    if I but call your name?
    Will you set the pris'ners free,
    and never be the same?
    Will you kiss the leper clean
    and do such as this unseen,
    and admit to what I mean
    in you, and you in me?

4. Will you love the 'you' you hide
    if I but call your name?
    Will you quell the fear inside,
    and never be the same?
    Will you use the faith you've found
    to reshape the world around
    through my sight and touch and sound
    in you, and you in me?

5. Lord, your summons echoes true
    when you but call my name.
    Let me turn and follow you,
    and never be the same.
    In your company I'll go
    where your love and footsteps show.
    Thus I'll move and live and grow
    in you, and you in me.

CELTIC
HYMN BOOK

212 With you alone

Colin Hodgetts
based on St Columba

James Leith Macbeth Bain
arr. Keith Duke

BROTHER JAMES'S AIR 86 86 86

1. With you a-lone, with none but you I jour-ney on my way. I have no fear when you are near, O King of dark and day. I am more safe with-in your hand than if guards round me stand.

2. You know the time left me to live
and Death will keep his hour;
did soldiers shield me with their steel
they could not stay his pow'r.
There's no defence in walls of stone
for he can beat them down.

3. My life I yield to your decree,
and bow to your control.
I peaceful am, for from your arm
no pow'r can wrest my soul:
no earthly omen can appal
the one who heeds your call.

4. When fear of death is overcome
then we are free to give
our lives to you to build on earth
your kingdom, there to live.
I celebrate the victory
your death has won for me.

213 You are the centre

Margaret Rizza

Margaret Rizza

1. You are the centre, you are my life, you are the centre, O Lord, of my life. Come, Lord, and guide me, Lord of my life, send me your Spirit, Lord of my life. You are the centre, Lord, of my life.

214 You are the maker

David Adam

Keith Duke

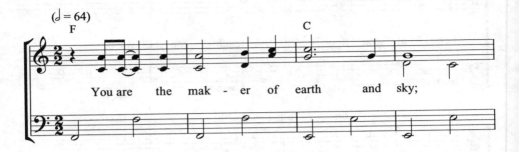

You are the mak - er of earth and sky;

you are the mak - er of birds that fly;

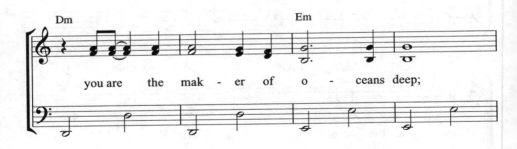

you are the mak - er of o - ceans deep;

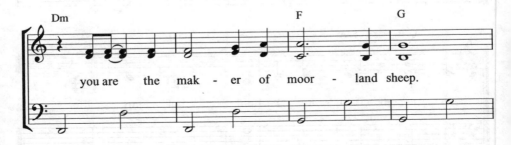

you are the mak - er of moor - land sheep.

215 You are the peace

David Adam

Angela Reith
arr. Keith Duke

1. You are the peace of all things calm,
you are the place to hide from harm,
you are the light that shines in the dark,
you are the heart's

2. You are the door that's open wide,
   you are the guest who waits inside,
   you are the stranger at the door,
   you are the calling of the poor.

3. You are my Lord, and with me still
   you are my love: keep me from ill.
   You are the light, the truth, the way,
   you are my saviour this very day,
   you are my saviour this very day.

216 You are the peace of all things calm

David Adam

Carolyn Beck
arr. Keith Duke

1. You are the peace of all things calm, you are the place to hide from harm. You are the light that shines in the dark, you are the heart's e - ter - nal spark.

2. You are the door that's open wide,
you are the guest who waits inside.
You are the stranger at the door,
you are the calling of the poor.

3. You are my Lord and with me still,
you are my love, keep me from ill.
You are the light, the truth, the way,
you are my Saviour this very day.

217 You, Lord, are in this place

David Adam

Keith Duke

2. You, Lord, are in my heart . . .

3. You, Lord, are in my mind . . .

4. You, Lord, are in my life . . .

CELTIC
HYMN BOOK

218 Your kingdom is upside down

John Morrow

John Morrow
arr. Keith Duke

1. Your king-dom is up - side down; you turn our life a - round: the poor are rich and the rich are poor, and the pure in heart are blest.

2. Your kingdom is upside down;
   you turn our life around:
   the strong are weak and the weak are strong,
   and all those who weep are blest.

3. Your kingdom is upside down;
   you turn our life around:
   the losers win and the winners lose
   and the peacemakers are blest.

4. Your kingdom is upside down;
   you turn our life around:
   the lost are found and the safe are lost
   and the merciful are blest.

219 You, whose breathing fills our bodies

Ray Simpson
echoing Angela Morgan

William Penfro Rowlands
arr. Keith Duke

BLAENWERN 87 87 D

(♩ = 120)

1. You, whose breath - ing fills our bo - dies, you, whose
pulse the worlds o - bey, tune our minds to
heed your rhy - thm, known a - long the star - ry way.
Swing the na - tions to your mea - sure, turn our hat - reds

in - to song; thrill us with your heal - ing
mu - sic, end - ing dis - cord, right - ing wrong.

2. You, whose order rules the atom, you, whose law propels the sea,
   bring the nations drowned in discord closer to your harmony.
   God of beauty, heal our sickness, God of love, our fractures mend;
   foster unity that binds us, rich to poor and foe to friend.

3. You, who light with heaven's glory, leaf and lake and cloud and star,
   light the hearts of all to justice, bring to faith those now afar.
   Pour your tender love upon us, you who fill both souls and space,
   turn us into sons and daughters, lifting up the human race.

INDEXES

Index of Authors, Composers, Arrangers and Sources of Music and Text

Alphabetical Index of Tunes

Metrical Index of Tunes

Scriptural Index

Index of Uses

Index of First Lines and Titles

Index of Authors, Composers, Arrangers and Sources of Music and Text

Alphabetical Index of Tunes

Metrical Index of Tunes

Scriptural Index

Index of Uses

Index of First Lines and Titles